ED... IT WAS MALIGNANT.

by Ed Montgomery

a cancer survival story

Ed Montgomery, Publisher
105 John Borden Street
Manteo, NC 27954

www.alwayscalled.com

1st Edition
1st Printing

Copyright © 2009

Printed in the United States of America

Cover photography by Kristi Midgette
Design by Nealy Hansford
Edited by Beth P. Storie

ISBN 978-0-984296-7-0-5

DEDICATION

I'd like to dedicate this book to my wife and my family for living through the hard part of cancer. There is a different, deeper sort of pain for those who must watch a loved one suffer and I am grateful that all of you stood strong with me. Thank you for being there and thank you for loving me.

ED... IT WAS **MALIGNANT.**

Those are the words my wife, Debbie, used to tell me I had cancer.

My initial response was, "oh." Not a shocked or even surprised "oh!" – more like someone had just told me I had spilled food on my shirt.

I never seem to get into a panic over big stuff. But put a slow driver in front of me when I'm on my way up to Home Depot and I freak out. Not the most logical representative of humanity, but then again, I am a guy.

Earlier in the day I had a tonsillectomy to remove a large growth inside my throat. The ear, nose and throat surgeon who handled the operation was the same doctor I met with just a week earlier at the recommendation of my family doctor. After examining me he told me that all my symptoms pointed to either lymphoma or nothing of consequence. "Nine out of ten times it's not cancer. So when we do the surgery we will do a frozen biopsy of the tonsil while you're on the table. If it's malignant we'll go down your esophagus and trachea and remove anything else that looks bad. If it's not, then we stitch you up and send you home because you just had your tonsils out." "Sounds like a plan," was my enthusiastic response.

I didn't feel anxious about this at all. I was in pretty good shape for a 45 year old and had none of the typical risk factors. I was never a smoker. I did chew tobacco some, but never habitually. Even smoked a pipe for a brief time, but quit that on the day I was working in my wood shop, looked down at a pile of sawdust at the foot of my table saw and caught sight of smoke and embers. After stomping it out, I decided I wasn't doing that anymore. Also no one in my family had ever had cancer. I had always been very healthy. Ate well, exercised, the whole bit. So while I was not looking forward to the pain everyone told me came along with a tonsillectomy, I didn't really expect to hear that I had anything else wrong with me. Surprise, surprise.

When I woke up from surgery in the recovery room, I first looked around for a clock, didn't find one, but saw a window and could tell that it was still light outside. Knowing what the plan was for surgery I figured the shorter the time in there the better, so the fact that it was still daylight was a good sign to me. A little while later after they moved me to a private room, I asked Debbie what the results were. "Inconclusive," she said though she looked at the floor when she said it. Turned out the doctor told her not to tell me because my throat was in a very fragile state and any trauma or stress could cause me some serious problems. I was still very groggy and extremely queasy so I didn't push it just then. We just sort of hung out while my mind cleared, stomach settled and I tried to figure out how to breathe.

"Didn't they remove stuff from my throat?" I asked. "Feels like they added a few layers."

After several hours of "recovery" the hospital decided that I should spend the night nearby since my throat was so swollen. Our home, which is on a small island off the coast of North Carolina in what is known as the Outer Banks, is more than an hour and half away from that particular hospital so they sent us over to the Ronald McDonald house which was just down the street. I guess it wouldn't be prudent to have to drive very far if I needed to get an airway cleared in a hurry.

I know my head was swimming, but I do remember the Ronald McDonald house there in Elizabeth City was a nice facility. It looked sort of like a very small hotel. Had a nice lobby when you walked in that was open to a TV area and just off of that was a kitchen and a couple of vending machines. Someone had put chocolate chip cookies out on a plate for guests like us. Of course I didn't eat any cookies and, come to think of it, didn't really want one. Normally I'd find that strange, but I was concentrating more on not throwing up and keeping air moving in and out of my lungs and avoiding anything that would add any more pain to the mix. We checked in and went down the hall to our room, which was a little smaller than most hotel rooms but plenty of space. It had two single beds, its own bathroom, a sink and mirror area, a chair and a closet. You could tell right away that almost everything in there was donated, because nothing matched. Furniture, linen and accessories: all sort of randomly put in there. But that eclectic mix made it feel nice and comfortable especially with the quilts and a stuffed doll for each bed. Yep, I held mine for awhile that night. Debbie was exhausted and I wanted to fall asleep, pass out or whatever just to skip some of the fun I was having at the moment, so we pretty much called dibs on our beds and climbed in.

I couldn't sleep. Go figure. I don't know how much time passed but Debbie got up and sat next to me sometime in the night. That's when she told me. She said she couldn't keep that from me and knew I could handle the truth and would want to hear it. She knows me very well. We had been married ten years, but since this was the second marriage for both of us, we have worked very hard at "getting it right," and honest communication was up at the top of the To Do List. Excellent choice on her part since I had been lying there, barely able to breathe, in pain and all I could think about was how the results could have been "inconclusive."

And so my relationship with cancer began, not knowing how serious it was, what the treatments would be, what my percentages were. But as we hugged each other and she cried, I did what I always do to reassure people: I made a joke.

"You know what this means?" I asked.

"No, what?"

"In a couple of years I get to win the Tour de France. No... wait... I still have both of my balls. I'll have to come up with something different."

I knew that no matter what the future held, things were going to be okay. This was just a bump in the road.

A couple of people suggested my wife and I start a journal on CaringBridge.org. What a terrific website, service and mission by those folks. It made it easy for us to keep in touch with friends and family without having to repeat myself a hundred times a day. It also made it easy for people to offer us encouragement and communication

ED...IT WAS **MALIGNANT.**

without feeling like they were being a burden. As our journal went a ong, people began to suggest that I write a book. I thought they just couldn't get enough of me having cancer, but each one said it was because reading the journal made them smile and even laugh. So apparently me having cancer is humorous to my friends.

Perhaps I should rethink my friend selection criteria, but for now I'll just put this experience in writing.

The pre-tonsillectomy picture (taken with my wife's cell phone)

I was born into a family of hearty, healthy and competitive individuals.

As the first boy in my generation, I was constantly encouraged to play all the sports my dad had participated in: baseball, basketball . . . pretty much anything that involved someone winning and someone losing. Except for football. My mom wasn't very keen on me hitting or getting hit, so instead I played soccer. I broke a leg twice and knocked out a couple of my own teeth in that sport over the years. Good thing I wasn't allowed to put on a helmet and pads. In high school I settled on running cross country and track, wrestled for a couple of years and played league basketball. For fun my friends and I were constantly playing any sport we could either imitate or create – tennis, baseball, rugby, football, skateboarding. We even made obstacle courses and ran relays to compete against each other like the ones on the TV show Superstars. Like so many other kids growing up in the 70's, being physically active was just what I did. College was more of the same with intramural basketball, softball, football, ultimate Frisbee and even lawn darts. Although there was a whole lot more beer involved in the college sports.

The fact that my dad was a fighter pilot in the Air Force meant I grew up enjoying great medical benefits, so we could hit the hospital for any old thing and did quite often. On top of accidents or getting physicals for sports, we'd go if I had so much as a runny nose. I got some terrific firsthand knowledge of how our muscular, skeletal and other internal systems work . . . and heal. No doubt my parents learned more about that stuff than they wanted. I became very comfortable, if that's the right word, in dealing with my own injuries. If there's blood, put pressure on it. If there's swelling, put ice on it. If an arm is bent in an unnatural direction, straighten it out. I wouldn't say I have a real high threshold for pain, but I do know that pain will go away quicker if I remove what's causing it in the first place. Like the time I stepped on a broken bottle while swimming in a creek near my house when I lived in Northern Virginia the summer before my freshman year in high school. The thing almost came through the top of my foot and caused one of my friends to turn green when he saw it. Still, I sat down on the dock and pulled it out by myself. Hurt like hell, but at least then I could put my shoe and sock back on and get back home to tell my mom we needed to run up to DeWitt Army Hospital at Ft. Belvoir. I even removed my own stitches when that one healed up and anyone who's done that will tell you that sounds like a much bigger deal than it is. Pulling stitches is a piece of cake.

After moving out on my own, though, my "family doctor" became the Emergency Room. Not that I was prone to body damaging accidents, which I was, but I was pretty much a healthy guy. Plus I felt like I knew my own body well enough and didn't really need someone else's opinion. I exercised off and on, ate well for the most part, had decent life habits (excluding college) and terrific genes. When my dad was about 65 years old he told me he still weighed what he weighed in high school. Of course he didn't look anything like he looked in high school, but the weight thing is something few people can claim. And no one in my family had ever been diagnosed with any deadly physical

malady. Basically, I never saw the need for regular visits to any particular doctor. If I got a sinus infection, I'd go to a "doc in the box" or something and get some antibiotics. So when I moved to Manteo, North Carolina, four years ago and opened my handyman business, I didn't run out and find a doctor so I could get regular physicals and such.

Recently, however, I had begun to think that someday I was actually going to begin aging and should start doing all those things aging people are supposed to do. Like get regular check-ups by a doctor who knew me by more than just an x-ray. Interestingly enough, I've always been pretty good about going to the dentist (except again for that college thing) and my current dentist helped me along with my maturation process _ specifically with what led to my cancer diagnosis.

At a cleaning appointment with him back in April, 2008 he noticed my left lymph gland was a bit swollen.

"You should have that checked by a doctor."

"Mmph?" (Why)

"A lot of reasons, but I'll give you just one: Leukemia."

"hmm gngmt omh inggmh." (I'll get right on it)

That gland had a tendency of swelling up whenever my allergies were bugging me then going back down when they weren't. Although it never really completely went away, I didn't think much of it.

Hind sight . . . I know.

Also sometime that spring I developed a hernia. Second time for me actually in the very same spot. There wasn't any pain or even any real discomfort, so I put that off for awhile, too. Besides, my handyman business was keeping me busy and I had just gotten the part as the comedian in The Outer Banks Music Showcase. Always one to enjoy making other people laugh, I had recently discovered how much fun it was to be on stage and hear an entire crowd bust up. Downright addictive. I had done a couple of comedies with the local little theater group and decided to try out for a "pro gig." The Showcase is a terrific, live, musical variety show that I saw for the first time back in 2003 and thought, "I would love to do that!" Four years later I got my chance and wound up on the cover of the playbill in a cow suit. I'm certain my kids were proud and showed all their friends. The show ran through October so I decided I'd schedule an appointment for a physical as soon as it wrapped up. Someone call Procrastinators Anonymous.

When Fall rolled around and the last shows were winding down I called the doctor and learned my physical would be a two part deal. The first one would be for most of the tests, exam and meeting the doctor and the second would be a follow up to go over the results of things. In that first appointment I heard all the things I normally heard. Blood pressure was great, heart rate fine, EKG fine, weight fine, prostate fine. I was just fine all over. Except of course for that slightly swollen lymph gland.

"Let's take a look at your throat," said Family Doc.

"Well, you've got this going on," as he tapped the back of my throat with a tongue depressor.

"What's going on?"

"You can't feel this?" more tapping.

"Of course I can feel that you're making me gag."

"No, I mean this lump."

"What lump?"

He handed me a mirror and asked, "You haven't had any trouble swallowing? Haven't felt anything in your throat?"

I angled the mirror while I said, "nope," and saw it for the first time. My left tonsil was about the size of the end of my thumb and my throat was about a third closed.

"Wow," was my honest response. "What is that?"

"You still have your tonsils," Doc stated.

"Yes, I do."

"They're coming out," and he said he would refer me to an ear, nose and throat surgeon to have a look at it and to do the tonsillectomy.

We discussed the fact that my tonsils didn't hurt, my throat wasn't sore and if he mentioned the possibility of cancer I don't remember it. He did say that the ENT should see it right away and they would call me as soon as they got that appointment scheduled. They would also handle scheduling my appointment with the surgeon for my hernia. I was due back with Family Doc in a week for my second appointment to go over blood work, etc. and that was that. I left wondering about that tonsil but not too worried about it and got busy with work that day. A couple of hours later the office called and said my appointment with the ENT wouldn't be until the middle of November, more than a month away. Sounded like nobody was really concerned about that lump.

But it was still a lump and I knew I didn't have tonsillitis. So being the computer savvy person I am, I checked out WebMD with my symptoms. Having said that I'd like to suggest that's not a good idea for anybody to do. It seems that no matter what you type in something 'horrible is first on the list for possibilities. A number of years ago I was up in Philly on business and someone noticed one of my pupils was much larger than the other. Nothing seemed to be wrong with my vision so I hadn't noticed. Several of the staff working with me hung over my shoulder as we went online to WebMD to see what was going on. Single dilated pupil, no change in vision and I read off the list of possibilities.

"Brain tumor, Encephalitis, Tumor in the chest, Meningitis, Glaucoma..."

A young guy over my right shoulder said, "Come onnnn glaucoma!" Turns out it was nothing. The eye doctor I went to back then said he had seen that happen with people who gardened and worked with certain fertilizers. I was in fact doing just that in our flower garden the

weekend before I traveled and everything else in me checked out just fine. No real explanation, but nothing to be concerned about.

When I saw the list of cancers listed online for my throat lump I clicked off and figured the same thing would happen here. Besides, if the doctor today thought it was really serious, I'd be seeing the ENT much sooner than in a month.

When I went back to Family Doc a week later, I met with the Nurse Practitioner and was told all my tests came back great. I was good to go and by the way when was my appointment to see the ENT? I told her and she said, "Oh? Why so late?"

"It was the earliest appointment he had open."

"I'll see if I can move that up and call you later today."

About an hour later my cell phone rang and the NP asked me if I was working or at home.

"I'm on a job, but flexible why?"

"Cancel your afternoon stuff. You need to go to Elizabeth City now. Your appointment with the ENT is in two hours."

Well, apparently somebody thought this could be serious after all.

Obviously, Debbie and I didn't get much sleep that first night at the Ronald McDonald House.

After she told me about meeting with the ENT surgeon while I was still snuggled in the black bliss of general anesthesia, we talked a little bit about how goofy it was for him to try to convince her not to tell me what they had discussed.

After all, I knew the plan going in, about the frozen biopsy being done while I was on the table,

so I was going to wake up and expect an answer.

The surgeon did tell her that he didn't want to add to my current trauma though and I understood his logic there.

The pain in my throat was ridiculous. On top of that it was so swollen I could barely breathe. That's the reason the folks at the hospital suggested we stay nearby. If I had a serious problem I would be right next door.

"I get his point, Debbie" I said. "If I were to start sobbing or something right now I'd just choke up and die. Or worse…tear up whatever they did in there and be in even more pain."

Debbie and I talked a little more, both of us glad to know what was what and anxious to get moving on to the next step. That's something I'm sure the doctor didn't know about us. Neither one of us is afraid of problems or challenges. We're happy when we're working on some-

ED...IT WAS **MALIGNANT.**

thing. We're not happy when we don't know what's wrong and can't at least try to fix it. Debbie and I agreed the best thing right then was to just get some sleep and take it on in the morning.

But I just couldn't breathe. And the pain medication that was supposed to last for four to six hours was getting me through about two. I couldn't lie down because it took neck muscles to turn my head even slightly and that just wasn't happening. Plus the only way I could breathe smoothly was to sit straight up or stand. So I stacked a bunch of pillows up against the headboard and sat there. Sort of sleeping, sort of gasping and sort of wincing. On top of all that they had pumped so many fluids into me during the operation that I had to go to the bathroom about every hour as well. Just lovely.

What occupied my mind most, though, was the money. Things were tight already and I knew even with insurance our out of pocket was going to be huge. And how much work would I miss? I had lined up several people to cover things for a week or so, but going forward would I even be able to supervise let alone do the jobs that came along? Then there's margin . . . or lack thereof. Paying other people to do the jobs was going to wreck that. What about keeping my customers happy? They did hire me to do the work after all. How would they react if someone else showed up? I was going to be doing some selling, that's for sure. Then there's managing the people doing the jobs. "People don't do what you expect, they do what you inspect." Phrases from my

past lives like that one started running through my mind.

As I thought about everything I began to feel a little better. Prior to opening up my own business, I had put together more than 20 years of sales experience. On top of that I had been a General Manager of Saturn retail facility and even a vice president at one of the largest title insurance corporations in the country. I'm good at sales and customer service and I'm good at managing people. I could do this. I even had a lot of work lined up all ready better than most folks in this area and line of work. Things were going to be whatever they would be, but I felt pretty sure it wasn't going to be a complete disaster.

I looked over at Debbie and thought, "she doesn't deserve this." When I considered things from her perspective, I just felt horrible.

Her father died when she was very young and her younger brother died in an accident before she turned 20. Now her husband has cancer. She was going to be carrying a lot of weight. It might not have been the first thing on her mind, but I know her well enough to guess that the thought of our future financial situation had made an appearance as well. She's going to have to get as much consulting work as she can get so we can stay above water. Which is going to mean being away from home and me most of the time. She's not going to like that at all.

I knew that I needed to do everything I could to make our burden just that: OUR burden. Together we'll get this done.

At that moment I was glad that I had been a long distance runner.

I knew about focusing ahead but not too far ahead. To the top of the next hill, the shoulder of the runner in front of me and finally on to the finish line. Pushing but conserving energy at the same time. This was going to be a long run and most would be uphill.

I can do this.

I will do this.

And I'm going to smile right through it.

I kept looking at the clock in the room hoping it would move up an hour between my glances, but it never did. Debbie couldn't get much rest either with me sounding like Darth Vader and performing all the pee Olympic stuff. Finally, with light coming in from the window she asked what time it was.

"6:45."

"Do you want to go ahead and head for home?"

"Might as well."

We got dressed. Stripped our beds (following the house instructions) and checked out.

"Leaving already?" the lady in the front room whispered to us as she stood by the desk in her nightgown and robe.

"Yep," we replied. "We have to drive all the way back to Manteo. Figured he could make it home okay now. Thanks for having us."

In the car I noticed the clock. 6:00 a.m. Hmmm. Looks like no one ever set the clock in the room for daylight savings time. Explains the

hostess' demeanor. She had just come out to start the coffee in the lobby area.

We drove a little and picked up coffee for Debbie and a diet coke for me from McDonalds. After some more time passed I decided I should call my kids before anyone else did. Yesterday before I woke up Debbie had called her two daughters, along with my mom and dad. She told me how each person took the news. It pained me to think of Ashley and Amy so worried and upset about me. Debbie said my dad was very calm and supportive, she even thought he was taking notes so he could pass the news along to my siblings appropriately. That's us Montgomerys: good in a crisis, dangerous at a party. But I know him well enough to know he was scared too. Even though I wasn't supposed to be talking, I told Debbie I was going to call all our kids and both my parents that day. I wanted them to know I was okay with this. That I was confident that whatever we faced was faceable. Reassurance. She agreed that would be good as long as I spread out the calls and rested my throat.

So I downed some more pain medication, waited a few minutes then started with my stepdaughters. I started with them because Debbie had already called them and I didn't want to put off calling myself. I told them we were headed home with lots of drugs. They both chided me for calling but said I sounded great.

"I thought you weren't supposed to be able to talk," said Ashley, at 29 the younger of the two.

"They don't know me too well do they, Ash?"

I called my daughter next knowing that a 21-year-old in college was sooo going to be asleep that early. But she answered right away.

"Hey Hil!" I graveled out. "Tonsils are out, but I have some tough news. I do have cancer."

"I had a dream that you did. What kind?"

"Squamous cell carcinoma of the throat. I'm going to look it up when I get home to see what the hell that means. But I think I'm going to be okay. I just wanted to let you know I'm good."

"Thanks, Dad. Now stop talking on the phone." For a Performing Arts major and the definitive Drama Queen, she was quite the cool customer.

I told her I would stop talking after I called Aaron. My son had recently made an incredibly mature decision to leave public school and attend a military boarding school to get his grades up and develop more self discipline. He was doing very well grade-wise and liked the school, but since he was "alone" and not near any family, I was anxious about breaking the news over the phone. But he's a very strong kid and easily more mature than I was at the age of 15, so after taking a break, I called him. Besides, it wasn't like there were any good ways to do this sort of thing. It just needed to be done. So I was direct with him too. Just told him straight out so he could hear that I was confident and

okay, despite the news.

"I have cancer."

"Well, that sucks."

"Yes it does, buddy. Yes it does."

We talked a little more; he sounded good and hung up. Then Debbie told me to shut up because my throat was not in as good a shape as it felt and I needed to rest it. Years of marriage, couples retreats and relationship books have helped me to understand the meanings behind her subtle nuances. I shut up.

I did call my mom and dad once I got home. It's strange hearing fear in your parent's voices. I told them that I just called to let them know I was doing ok. I've got cancer, but I'm cool. Doctors are going to be working on it and I'm going to do whatever I need to do to get better. Things are going to be just fine. When my dad said he felt a whole lot better after my call it made me smile. To reassure the guy that had reassured me so often in my life was kind of nice.

If you've heard that the older you are when you get your tonsils out the worse the pain is, then you heard correctly, and I was older than I thought when mine came out. I have dislocated a shoulder twice, a hip once, broken numerous bones including my jaw.

Nothing hurt like this. At least nothing hurt as long as this.

I t just never seemed to let up. I looked in the mirror with a small flash-light and the entire back and sides of my throat looked like scorched earth. No lie. They don't stitch you up after a tonsillectomy, they cauter-ize everything. Looked to me like they used an acetylene torch to do mine. Maybe coated it with lighter fluid and tossed in a match. I could imagine the surgeon saying, "We're done, let's close him up. Everyone step back. . . ." Whoooff!

Once the effects of the anesthesia wore off completely, I was down to liquid hydrocodone (vicodin) and meperidine tablets. I was sup-posed to take 15 ml of the liquid every four hours and if I had severe pain, I could take one of the pills every four hours as well. I could sleep maybe two hours before waking up in agony again. Debbie would roll over and look at me standing next to the bed, leaning over making fists in the sheets with my head down.

"You going to be okay?"

"Yep."

"Anything I can do?"

"Kill me."

"Anything else?"

"No...I'll take more medication in a little bit."

"I'm sorry you hurt."

"Me, too."

My nights and days kind of blended for the first couple of days. When I don't feel well I tend to just sleep. So I sort of repeated that pattern for a day or two. If I was awake and had just taken some pain meds we actually had normal conversations and watched TV. I was a bit wasted during those times though, so I'm sure for her it was like talking to a drunk.

Pain management became job #1 over the next two weeks. I stayed tight to the four hour doses of hydrocodone and did what I could to stretch out between doses of the heavier stuff. Reading through the materials the nurse at the hospital gave us regarding recovery from a tonsillectomy, I was pretty skeptical of ice packs on the back of my neck. That wasn't where it hurt at all. But when I tried it I was pleasantly surprised by the relief it provided. We have this really cool device that is like a long sock filled with some sort of very small beads that you

can stick in the microwave for heat or the freezer for cold and then you just wrap it around wherever you need it. It folded perfectly around the back of my neck and really did tone down the pain a lot. It wasn't gone, but I didn't need to take any of the other stuff and could function enough to write thank you notes and talk to folks.

One of the first times I was up and around during the daylight, I looked up squamous cell carcinoma on the internet. I think Debbie had already, but she listened as I told her that it is the most common form of cancer and one of the most treatable. Pretty good news. The articles I read explained the process for treating throat cancer and I was done with step one: getting my tonsils and any tumors out. Sweet! Now I just have radiation and chemo to go! Terrific...

Several days after the operation my ENT called to talk to us, and he thought to give me the news. I told him Debbie had told me that first night and he really should have as well. He reiterated that his concern was for the additional trauma the stress could cause to my throat. Knowing both of us had seen my throat, I had to agree with him. Everything hurt it, let alone any stress. But it would have been more stressful not to know and I think he understood that too.

He went on to tell me all about the surgery. After getting the biopsy back they did what they had planned and looked down my esophagus and windpipe, not finding any additional tumors or bad looking spots, and then took tissue samples from around the tonsil areas. They also did a fine needle aspiration to get a sample of the fluid in my lymph glands. Cancer cells were found in the surrounding tissue of the tumor but not anywhere else in my throat. And cancer cells were found in the swollen lymph gland, but not in others. ENT Doc said this was good news and he felt they got as much as they could have without doing a procedure called a neck dissection a really, really nasty operation that involves peeling your neck and face up and removing almost everything there except the spine. He described it in much more detail but had me at the face peeling. I was glad we didn't do it.

He confirmed what I had read on the web regarding throat cancer; my prognosis was good. He told me my treatment would be decided upon between him, a radiation oncologist, and a hematology oncologist, but he thought it would combine radiation and chemo for about two months and that would be that. I should recover fully, but I would be seeing him on a regular basis for the next five years.

We talked about the cancer center and doctors here on the Outer Banks and settled on the two doctors he would call to get things moving. We were going to be seeing a lot of doctors over the next couple of weeks. Get the credit cards ready.

Now, I really enjoy living in a small town. Manteo has only around 2,000 people, so it is a really small town and I love it. Word gets around fast, especially with things like illnesses. It starts with the church. Debbie and I had told our church the Sunday before my operation that I

was getting the tonsillectomy and why. Everyone was immediately very supportive and started offering to bring food, etc. when I got home. After the surgery the phone rang off the hook and people came by to find out how things went. In the midst of the physical pain in my throat and the knowledge that I had cancer, I remember how great it felt to have so many friends right there. Everyone was offering their heartfelt concerns, grief and then confidence in us to pull this off. One friend of ours came over with her young daughter to visit me. They had just come from a birthday party and wanted to bring me some balloons. The balloons had 'Happy Birthday' written on them, but they didn't think I'd mind. We all laughed and laughed and hugged. Debbie and I were not alone and we knew we had all the resources we needed without even knowing what the needs would be yet.

After I was more mobile and got outside, people wherever I went would come up and hug me, tell me they heard the news and asked how I was doing. Up at Ace Hardware, I'm in there a couple of times a day every day due to my Handyman gig and I'm friends with most of the employees. They're all great people and would tell me they told all their churches about me, their family and so on. I had people praying for me all over the place. They would also share stories they knew of other people who had been through this same cancer and how they were doing fine. It really encouraged me. I was at the checkout counter talking with one of the cashiers about things when a lady behind me,

ED... IT WAS **MALIGNANT.**

who I had never met, asked me, "You have cancer?"

"Yep, but the prognosis is very good."

"Well bless your heart." She hugged me then asked, "What's your name?"

"Ed Montgomery."

"Well, Ed, I'm going to put you on my church's prayer list if that's okay."

"Absolutely it's ok."

I just LOVE small towns.

No, the President didn't stop by.

All our kids came down for the weekend for the first time after hearing I had cancer. Sheesh.

It had been over a week since my tonsillectomy and I was doing a little better with all the pain management stuff. I could only eat mushed up, lukewarm food but was swallowing well enough and felt much better. Not good, really, but better. I was really looking forward to seeing all of them, too. I know this sort of news, even with a good prognosis, was tough on all of them and I wanted them to get to see firsthand that I was okay. Still here.

All of our children live up in the Richmond, Virginia, area. Debbie's two, Amy and Ashley, are both out of college and married. Amy to Sean and Ashley to John. I decided that whenever I referred to the two sons-in-law, I could call them "Diddy." Short for P-Diddy, short for Puff Daddy,

ED... IT WAS **MALIGNANT.**

a nickname for rapper/entrepreneur Sean Combs, who's clothing line is of course "Sean John."

Clever, I know.

Amy and Sean are the parents of our first two grandchildren, Ava and Annabelle and they are incredible. I swear if there was a way to go straight to being a grandparent I'd have done it. Then we have my two children, Hilary and Aaron. Hil is in her fourth year at Virginia Commonwealth University as a performing arts major and has been in several main stage productions. Aaron is a high school sophomore out at Hargrave Military Academy. The choice he made to go there had me really nervous at first, but so far so good, the kid's made Dean's List just about every grading period so far. And he made varsity cross country and varsity lacrosse. Above and beyond all the typical parental bragging subjects, all of our children are just plain terrific people and a lot of fun to be around. These family visits are truly entertaining and a joy, even when their dogs come.

And these are big, big dogs I'm talking about. There's a chocolate lab and two American Mixed Breeds that are mostly lab and blue tic. Each one pushing one hundred pounds. When they invade the house, our little beagle does her best to assert her dominance by yelping, howling and lashing out randomly at all of them. If they ever really notice her attacks, I think she'll be in serious trouble.

As each car full of people and animals arrived, there were a lot of

teary hugs. Everyone was supportive and yet still 'normal' to me. Which is to say they picked on me.

Amy, who is often embarrassingly direct, said, "Mom married a younger guy so you could take care of her when she was sick! You're screwing this up."

As I talked about the effects of radiation, Hilary pointed out, "Dad, you're already going bald. So what?"

Then Aaron chimed in, "It's not like it's going to hurt your looks."

Made me feel good all over.

No, really. It did.

While there was a serious sort of cloud over everything, those comments were what I was hoping to hear. What I needed to hear. I could tell they were doing just fine.

Of course it's nice to be surrounded by people who are pretty much like you are. This group enjoys finding the humor in things and so do I. So it reassured me when they made light of the situation. Debbie, however, is a little different. While she has a terrific sense of humor, it's not where she runs when things get bad. She takes serious things seriously. She also processes everything in life carefully before moving ahead - another difference between us and thank God for that, because I've been in more proverbial ditches because I'm "all thrust and no vector" as my fighter-pilot father has put it. Everyone has a different way of dealing with bad news. She and I do it differently, and that can be a good thing.

At dinner we were all sitting around the table with everyone eating this awesome meal produced by Amy's creative culinary mind along with multiple supporting partners. But I, the sick one, the supposed center of attention on this visit, didn't get to enjoy it. I had some mashed potatoes I think and something else bland and soft. Not that it was completely lousy. All I had to do was think back to two days earlier and how my throat felt, what I was capable of eating then and of course I began to feel like this was quite the celebration meal. Multiple courses with lots of fixins'! Sort of . . . I had to really use my imagination with that one. What I didn't have to imagine was how great it was to have the family packed in around our dining room table. Eating, talking about what was going on in all their lives, watching them smile and laugh with (or at) each other.

Hilary had come down with her boyfriend and although he had met everyone once at a party hosted by Ashley and John, he hadn't been locked in with the group yet. He held his own quite well actually and looked pretty comfortable for the most part. He handled being quizzed, sometimes subtlety, sometimes not, on what he was studying in college, how he met Hilary, what his intentions were, etc. Aaron B., as Hilary calls him so we don't confuse him with our Aaron M., is Jewish, and Hilary was telling us how she recognized Yom Kippur back in Oc-tober with him and did all the "fasting stuff." Aaron B. kind of shrugged and said with some sheepish sarcasm, "well, there's some prayer and repentance in there, too."

"And did you do any praying and repenting in there?" I asked Hilary.

"Well . . ." she started slowly.

It was kind of obvious that she hadn't put much effort into that part and being the type of Dad I am, I wanted her to focus a little more on the reason than on the ritual.

"You know last year when people asked me what I gave up for Lent," I started. "I told them I gave up giving up stuff." There was some chuckling.

"And now," I waved my arms open dramatically, "I have cancer." Lots of laughter and why not? That's pretty funny stuff. Everybody laughed.

Except my wife.

We made eye contact and I knew I had just done something that hurt her. She still smiled and all, not wanting everyone else to think she wasn't just as entertained, but I knew it.

I caught her alone later and apologized for it. I told her I knew this was scary for her and I was inconsiderate of her feelings with that joke. She said she knew I used humor as a tool for dealing with things, that was okay, but she wasn't there yet. We hugged and I told her I'd do better in the future. Around her I made sure to be myself but not act like I didn't have a care in the world. Because I have a lot of cares: her, for one.

CaringBridge entry for Wednesday, November 19, 2008

Hello Friends and Family,

As most of you know Ed was diagnosed with cancer a couple of weeks ago. The surgeon removed his tonsils and adenoids and removed a mass from his throat. The mass was malignant and there were also cancer cells in his lymph gland on the left side of his neck.

The outpouring of love and concern has been wonderful. We have started this site to keep everyone updated and informed.

Yesterday Ed had his first appointment with the radiation oncologist at the OBX Cancer Center in Nags Head. We were relieved to learn that the treatments would be done here instead of in Elizabeth City. The first step in the planning session was to visit our dentist to confirm that Ed does not need any dental work done before treatments begin. Our dentist had a concern about an old injury to one of Ed's front teeth and sent us to a root canal dentist. He said the root canal can wait. Whew!

The next step was to visit a general surgeon today to find out if Ed should have a hernia repair done prior to beginning radiation/chemo treatments. The surgeons and the oncologist decided that this would be best. Ed is scheduled for surgery next Tuesday. The recovery time should be about 2 – 3 weeks.

Tomorrow Ed will have a CAT scan done at the Cancer Center and will have his initial meeting with the medical oncologist who will be doing the chemo treatments. The CAT scan will be used to build the template for radiation. The turnaround time on the build is about 48 hours, but there will be 2 weeks of quality control done before Ed begins treatments.

On Friday we go to Norfolk for a PET scan. This is a full body scan to make sure the cancer has not invaded any other part of his body.

Right now Ed is feeling better. His throat is still very sore, but he is finally eating people food (instead of mushed up stuff). The focus is now on gaining as much weight as possible before he starts chemo/radiation. As you know Ed is not a real bulky person to begin with, so any excessive weight loss is unacceptable! To that end the oncologist has already warned that since the neck radiation will cause swallowing problems, a feeding tube may need to be surgically inserted into Ed's stomach during the next several weeks if he begins to lose too much weight. I'm trying to help by baking cookies every night to fatten him up. Unfortunately, I'm eating as many as he is!

My plan is to update this site daily. Thank you for caring and for supporting us during this bump in the road of life.

Debbie

responses

Ed and Debbie,

I am saddened to hear about the cancer,

but I know your strong faith and determination will see you through the trials you are about to endure. Thank you for including me here, and I will check back daily for updates. My thoughts and prayers are with you from afar.

Love to you both, Lisa

Hey there bro,

I have been thinking about all the stories about things you did while at Virginia Tech . . . so this might not need to be said, but then again . . .

if you need a feeding tube, please be sure to ask the doctor before you "chug" anything, ok?! Ok.

Donya

Hey Ed and Debbie . . .

Mom and I are glad to hear of your steady progress toward complete healing and are praying for our Father's hand to guide all the caregivers with divine wisdom as they minister to you in body, soul and spirit. **We love you!**

Major

Debbie and Ed, Positive Vibes from Vermont!

If any two people can handle a bump in the road, it's you two.

Please take strength in knowing how much you are thought of, prayed for and loved.

Kelli

Hey Ed and Debbie!

I just got your email with this update.

I'm praying for Ed's strength and bulk

to be maintained and built up before the treatment begins. I'm also praying for Debbie's strength as a caregiver. Hope you enjoyed the potato soup.

Love, Kevin, Wendy and Josiah

Hi dear friends,

What unexpected news —

take a deep breath and plunge in with your faith and the blessings of modern medicine.

We send our love and support!

Kay

Hi Ed and Debbie,

Thanks, Debbie, for setting up CaringBridge. What a marvelous method for all of us keeping up with Ed's progress. We won't have to pester either of you with "what's new?" When one is not feeling quite up, it is difficult to tell friends "Not now . . . ." Ed, what a bummer!

We wonder why bad things happen to good people.

You are good people, but you have the gumption to persevere!

The good thoughts and prayers from Ar and myself are with you constantly.

Our love to both of you!

Arlene and Harry

This site is such a great idea. With the great amount of people concerned about you both,

this is a wonderful way to keep us updated without "bugging."

My thoughts and prayers are always with you.

Sue

Ed & Debbie,

Bill and I have been thinking and praying for you since we learned of Ed's surgery and all that you are going through. We pray for strength for each day as you undergo so many tests.

We miss you and will continue checking updates in CaringBridge.

Sylvia

Wow Ed!!

Not really the way I would have hoped to reconnect with you.

Nonetheless, I'm glad you and Debbie thought to include me in your "support" group . . . . Terry's and my prayers will be with you. We will stay in touch and keep them headed your way. It has been a long time since we ran together . . . when you are ready to do it again let me know . . . nothing better than a sunset run along the Pacific.

Take care and Godspeed on the treatments.

Ken

Dear Ed and Debbie,

I just got the word through CaringBridge and was just floored.

Big Brother, I have not always been regular when it comes to praying, but you will be in my thoughts and prayers every day.

Debbie, I like that you called this a bump in the road; Ed is a resilient guy and I know he's going to beat this. Fattening him up sounds like a winner, assuming his superman metabolism allows it. If the oncologist approves, I recommend washing down those cookies with some nice Weeping Radish. It always helps me put on some extra pounds. Love you!

L&R, Blake

responses

Mom and Ed, I have written a limerick in Ed's honor.

There once was a man named Ed,
The tonsillectomy made his throat red.
He needs to gain weight so he eats,
His friends make super good treats,
Mom, make sure he is well fed!

Amy

CaringBridge entry for Thursday, November 20, 2008

Good news today! We visited the medical oncologist this morning. He has determined that Ed does not need chemo!!!! The only thing that would change his mind is the PET scan being done tomorrow in Norfolk. If the scan shows any cancer cells beyond the areas we are already aware of then he will reassess. Keep those prayers coming!

This afternoon the radiation oncologist made a mold of Ed's head and neck in order to build the radiation template. We should be good to go sometime after Thanksgiving. The surgery for the hernia is still scheduled for Tuesday. We will be spending Thanksgiving at home this year instead of making our annual trip to Northern Virginia. If Ed is up to it we hope to go to Richmond the weekend after the holiday to see all of our kids and our precious grandbabies. That would cheer anyone up!

Thanks for all of your messages and good wishes. We sincerely appreciate the support.

Debbie

responses

An email from a looong-time friend:

" . . .have you checked out hats.com?"

Dwayne

Ed: Best wishes and healing thoughts in your recovery.

You can now join a growing community of survivors here on the Outer Banks.

Janet and I will follow your progress.

Tom

Ed, so sorry to hear the news.

Paige and I will keep you in our prayers. I have no doubt that everything will turn out fine. I've known you long enough to know that this will only be a speed bump and not a roadblock. In fact, if I know you at all, you will come out of this stronger and better.

Quite often you have turned life's lemons into lemonade and I'm sure you'll do it again. . . .

Chris

No che mo
No che mo
No che mo

I'm doing the no chemo dance –

Donya

I was shocked and saddened to hear of your illness.
I hope you keep your positive attitude and emotional fortitude.

As always, keep yourself and everyone around you laughing!

God Bless, Vicque

Dear Debbie and Ed;

Yay! No Chemo!! We continue to keep you in our thoughts and prayers and

await our "helping orders."

Love, Sue & John

CaringBridge entry for Friday, November 21, 2008 6:45 am

Well, we're up early this morning and runnin' off to Norfolk. I'm going to have a full body PET Scan done this morning. This will serve two purposes: determine if there are any other cancer-active areas in me, and help design the computer program for my radiation treatment. Apparently radiation treatment has come a long way in the last decade or so. Computer-controlled equipment is used to pinpoint treatment within a couple of millimeters of a three dimensional area. This helps target the heavy doses where they belong while minimizing damage to surrounding "good" tissues. Like my brain for instance. Not that I use much of it, but the doctors say it's a good thing for most people to avoid frying it. This will also help reduce the nasty side effects. Notice how I said "reduce" there and not "eliminate." My Radiation Doc seems to go to great length to describe how bad things "could" be then tell me some people don't have it that bad. Setting expectations I guess.

The chemo doctor was kind of similar in that he went a little overboard on describing the side effects of chemo and radiation. He actually used the word "medieval" when talking about a chemical they wouldn't be using on me. Maybe it's just fun to talk about it. I don't know.

At any rate we're hoping this scan shows I'm clean except for that left lymph gland and some tissue surrounding the space where a tonsil used to be. Thanks for all the great notes and comments folks. And, yes Dwayne, I've checked out hats.com and will pick up something totally embarrassing to my kids.

. . . maybe something with a feather in it. . . .

It snowed on the way up to Norfolk.
We did not move down here for the snow. . . .

responses

Ed and Debbie,
I have to admit that Roger and I are just hearing about Ed's cancer for the first time.
So we are shocked (to put it mildly).
Thank you for including us as part of the group of family and friends to be updated and to stay in communication with Ed throughout his recovery. Ed, you are in our prayers.
Sending a huge hug to you.
Kathy

Amazing and fabulous to hear about the radiation advances they have made.
Here's praying for the smallest effective target being discovered in the full body scan.
Hugs, Anne and John

I've been in your position and am a survivor as you will be!!!
The best medicine I had was my sense of humor, and that is going to be yours as well.
In the meantime, I'll keep thinking of all the material you're going to come up with during this time and how you'll use it positively!!
Love, Sheila

Hey there bro, you want a hat that will embarrass the kids? I CAN DO THAT!!!
Mom can knit you a comfort hat, and I'll knit the one you wear around kids.
Phil has one he calls The Hat of Great Intelligence. I won't tell you what the kids call it.
It's based on your basic Joker hat.
I'm thinking that might be a good look for you.
Love you, Donya

Ed and Debbie,
Have a pattern, needles and blue chinchilla yarn: softest going!
One hat coming up!!
Love, Yo Momma

The picture is great. It only reinforces how much we love and care about you.
No doubt you'll be a special patient to all the medical staff.
Keep them laughing. You are gifted in so many ways. We will read all your memos. You guys are soooo hep! Both of you are in our daily thoughts and prayers.
Love, Jane and Harold

Journal

CaringBridge entry for Friday, November 21, 2008

Well, the PET scan was pretty uneventful from a participants view. Another night of fasting followed up by an IV of radioactive glucose. The Tech hooked me up to the IV then brings out this syringe wrapped in an antique thermos and says, "It's a very low radioactive charge, you don't have anything to worry about."

Pointing to the lead thermos I replied, "And apparently you don't either."

We'll hear something next week from my radiation oncologist. Funny thing: a couple of years ago I repaired some loose shingles on his roof.

Gee, I hope they're holding up okay. . . . .

responses

Hi Ed,

So glad that the PET Scan is behind you and glad also that you were able to joke around with the staff. No great surprise there. This communication system is really amazing.

It is obvious that you have friends and family rallying around you in full force.

Thanks be to God! What great news about not needing chemo. I am so thankful to learn that. Jeff and I want to be helpful in any way we can. We both love you guys very much.

Blessings, Sandy

Let me know if you develop any "special powers" after treatment.

I saw this Boris Karloff movie once . . . .

David

Special powers? David said something about special powers. You already have special powers... do you get more? So, no word yet on the PET scan or you would have printed it here.

So, did you take your dog for the scan or does the hospital provide a pet of its own?

Does the pet have to walk up and down while looking at you intently, or does the hospital provide a moving sidewalk thingy? If the pet is a cat, how do they make it do anything? Wow modern medicine is amazing!

Love you bro, Donya

Ed –

Doreen and I had not heard you were ill. We wish you a speedy recovery. I must say that the hospital picture is priceless.

It reminds me of one of your old outfits from an ATO Halloween Party!!

Some things never change . . . . Get well soon my friend. I hope to speak to you soon.

Love, John

Ed, sorry to hear this news, but for you it probably will be nothing more than a bump in the road. While I didn't get to spend much time working with you, I have a load of great Ed stories I enjoy telling everyone on a regular basis.

I am now a guy people come to for energy, and I owe you for that. THANKS!

You are in my thoughts and my prayers, and I look forward to hearing what is going on once you have fully recovered.

All the best, David

Crazy Ed Montgomery: We did not know until we received this e-mail from "1-Easy".

Anytime one hears the C-word it sends chills,

and I'm glad to hear it's treatable and the outcome looks good.

You have touched many people with your humor and great outlook on life. Kay and I continue to this day to tell friends hilarious stories about you from Tech. Keep up your great attitude. Let me know if we can help, and we will keep you in our prayers.

Steve

CaringBridge entry for Friday, November 25, 2008

Ed's update: So, today was hernia operation day. Got to the hospital at 7 a.m. after an hour and half drive, definitely not one of the perks of living on an island, and finally went into the OR around 9:15. This being a repair to a previous hernia operation meant it took a very long time in surgery and I came to around noon. My surgeon said things went very well and even had pictures! I get to see them again at the post op visit and hope to get copies to send to my little brother in Turkey. Gore is cool.

I couldn't convince the nurse that I wasn't in any real pain, so she had me take a vicodin (sp?) and in a few minutes I puked. Lovely. And a nice exercise for abdominal muscles that have just been separated by CO_2, stuffed with Kevlar mesh and stitched up.

We hung out for a little while longer then headed home, and I threw up again . . . right down the side of Debbie's car. Did get a tailgater to back off though, so it wasn't a complete waste.

Now it's time to spend a couple of days taking it easy and recovering.

Debbie's update: The only good thing about being the patient is Ed got to sleep all day. I waited until he went into surgery at 9:15 (talking all the way to the OR) and then I went downstairs for cafeteria food for breakfast. When I got back to the second floor the fire alarms were going off and a "Code Red in the OR" announcement was being broadcast over the 2nd floor intercom. I wasn't allowed to go to the surgical waiting room but was moved into the closest room with three other people and the door was shut. We had a view of the three fire trucks as they pulled up to the front doors. We were finally released from captivity and told it was a false alarm where they are doing some demolition in the old OR. Whew! Too much excitement for me!

The surgeon came to see me at 11:30 to tell me Ed was fine and proceeded to show me pictures of the hernia repair from the laparoscopic camera's point of view. For all I knew I could have been looking at a map of Indonesia. There were hills and valleys and roadways and farmland . . . anyway it was lost on me. . . .

Ed was queasy from the time he woke up until we got home four long hours later! He is resting in the recliner now in front of the fire and the TV eating a delicious dinner our friends Sandy and Susan brought to us. He needs to rest for several days and then the radiation treatments begin sometime after Thanksgiving.

Thanks for all your emails! We are truly blessed!

        -Debbie

responses

You learned something useful –

Vicodin does the same thing to Anne and it is no fun.
Put that on your do not give me list!

John

Ed,

So glad your surgery went well and that you still have your sense of humor.

Please don't ever lose that. Take care.

Love ya. Barb

Debbie and Ed –

I would place bets on the fact that Ed talked through surgery.

It happens you know. Very glad, though, that it went so well.
We hope to see you soon, and as usual you are in our hearts.

Love, Ed & Lynda

Glad to see you have kept your wonderful sense of humor through all this.

Keep your chin up and get well soon – we need another visit to Belize.

Ray

Prior to all of this, I had only had surgery once.

That was for that hernia I gave myself while chopping down trees alone in the backyard of our house in Richmond. No, I wasn't using a dull axe. It was a dull chain saw. I had a nice, tall tree tied off and cut the base. But the wind decided to start taking the tree in a direction I did not want it to go, so I grabbed the rope, ran to the appropriate location, planted my feet against another tree and pulled hard. Very hard. I was successful in guiding the tree to the right spot for landing, but pulled something in my groin and that was that.

This time I have no idea how I got the hernia. Maybe I coughed too hard or something. I do tend to lift heavy things at odd angles here and there in my job, so it could have been anything. At any rate this hernia repair would be the second operation I would have in a month, and I learned something about the side effects of general anesthesia that are ncreased the longer or more often you are exposed to the anesthesia.

Things can taste "funny". Not "funny" (ha-ha), "funny" (lousy).

I noticed this the very first night, but figured I was still feeling the effects of surgery and just ate anyways. As the days went by and things remained very odd tasting, I decided to call my ENT and ask if they had any idea why this might be. I hadn't noticed it before and was worried that it might have something to do with my throat somehow.

"It's the anesthesia," said the nurse over the phone.

"How long does it normally last?" I asked.

"Could last up to a month."

I thought about that and realized that would put me on top of Christmas.

Lovely.

Here I was supposed to be trying to gain as much weight as possible before radiation treatments started and everything tasted like it was dull. Sort of a metallic mud thing. Very difficult to pin down, but not appetizing to say the least. So my throat had healed up enough to eat food I actually chewed, but now it all tasted bad and would through-out the process because Radiation Doc told me that the first side effect I would notice from radiation treatment was ... wait for it ... a metallic taste in my mouth. After that my taste buds would deteriorate and pretty much everything would be nasty until a month or so after treat-ments finished. All I could do was lower my head and slowly shake it side to side.

Another dynamic that occurred at this point was that the ice pack around my neck was moved to my groin. I know that doesn't sound like a pleasant thing, but after those surgeries it was a relief to have that thing tucked onto just the right spot while I sat in the recliner clicking through cable channels until my mind was numb. Among other things. I think I used that thing steadily for three whole weeks between the two spots.

Not the remote, the ice pack.

Thanksgiving 2008

Seated L to R: Aaron Ben, Hilary, me, Ava, Debbie, Aaron and Stephanie.
Standing L to R: Sean, Amy, Annabelle, Ashley and John.

Journal

CaringBridge entry for November 26, 2008

Well, another night of waking up every four hours with some sort of sharp pain is over. Kinda impressive actually since that's the time frame listed on my prescriptions. Recovery is going as planned, and I'll be back to normal by Friday or Saturday. So we'll head up to Richmond to see all the kids and grandkids this weekend!

I probably won't have any new updates for several days since there's nothing much happening until I hear from the radiation oncologist about a start date for treatment. Y'all have a wonderful Thanksgiving and thank you, thank you, thank you for all the prayers, thoughts, and kind words. It means an awful lot to me.

Ed

responses

Hey Y'all. . . just wanted to send a note of love and thanks

'cause you are part of my "what I'm thankful for" list on this Thanksgiving.

The Spirit reminds me of a couple of verses that have brought me comfort over the years. . . . I hope they do for you too:

Romans 8:18 – For I reckon that the sufferings of this present time are not worthy to be compared with the glory which shall be revealed in us.

1 Corinthians 4:17-18 – For our light affliction, which is but for a moment, worketh for us a far more exceeding and eternal weight of glory; while we look not at the things which are seen, but at the things which are not seen: for the things which are seen are temporal, but the things which are not seen are eternal.

Major

Hey Ed & Debbie,

So sorry to hear about your illness – just want you to know you are in my thoughts and prayers. You guys are great folks and are an inspiration to me and I am sure many others.

Stay strong and remember the Lord never gives us more than we can handle.

Linda

Hi Ed,

Michael and I are just sitting here watching an old *Rocky* movie and thought we'd wish you and your family a

Happy Turkey Day! We are keeping you in our prayers and think of you all often.

Renee

We will be thinking of you all today and raising a glass to you in thanks.

Take care and know that we are sending you all our love and hugs.

Jo Dee

Hi son, thanks to you and Debbie for getting us involved with CaringBridge.

You and she have a great attitude toward your situation, and we're confident that all will work out well in the end. It was great to talk with you on Thanksgiving Day, especially to learn that chemotherapy won't be needed!

Keep up the fight!

Dad & Lucia

CaringBridge entry for December 3, 2008

I went to the dentist again today. This time to get fitted for these nifty mouth plates so I can do my own fluoride treatments at home . . . starting a few days before my radiation treatments, continuing one every day, five minutes at a time until treatment is over. I asked, "Why?" Seemed an innocent enough question, but the answer came with these great brochures describing things like mucositis, demineralization and osteonecrosis. Now, I never took Latin, but I can still read "bones" and "dead" in that last one. Can I do the fluoride thingy twice a day? And actually I can. Depends on what the radiation oncologist recommends.

Other than that I've had no news other than they're working on my radiation program and we'll get going in a week or two. Radiology Doc told me the good news was that now I'll be able to actually eat my Christmas dinner . . . yippee . . . I should be up to about 80% recovered from my hernia operation by then.

Meanwhile, it's just working as usual: finishing up an art studio, remodeling a kitchen & bathroom, several interior painting jobs and a few other odds & ends.

Thanks again to everyone who's sent support. I love all y'all and truly appreciate it!

Ed

responses

Hi Ed (and Debbie) . . . I'm so sorry to hear of your illness . . . you're in my prayers each day.

Many, many people recover from this kind of diagnosis, and I pray that you will be at the top of that list!

Peace and Blessings,
Connie

So good to see you out and about — and enjoying Family Night dinner again together at church.

All the medical news is encouraging —God is good — All the time!

Susan and Joe

Hi kids! Good to hear how things are going and that you are keeping busy as usual. Reading your emails reminds me of how positive you both are and how much I enjoyed my time with you both. **Such a treasure to be such a positive force in the world.** It's been 'cold' out here in SF this week — lots of complaining after last week when it was near 80 and we were at the beach! Hugs from both of us.

Luv, Jo Dee & Jeff

Hi Ed and Deb, The news sounds very positive to me! Keep it up and build up your strength for the radiation, so it will be easier for you.

You will beat this stuff, I am very sure.

You both are in my thoughts and prayers.

Mark

Dear Ed and Debbie,

So glad your surgeries are behind you and things are looking good. You have been in our prayers daily. **You have been blessed with so many friends, and with all their prayers and help you will recover.** Glad you were able to make the trip to Richmond to spend Thanksgiving with the family. The granddaughters are adorable and I know lots of fun. We love both of you.

Ray and Karen

Thanks to Glenn for always passing along news about RMG alumns. We will include you on our prayer list and trust the Lord will heal you in short order.

Our hearts go out to you and wish you well.

If we can do anything for you, please do let us know.

Debby and Annie

Just opened the last update and it sounds great.

Sorry we have not been in touch lately but been away with friends to Alexandria, Virginia, for the week. Had a ball and froze. Back at the old grind now. Will attempt to keep in touch as much as possible. We will be away again right after Christmas for another week. Janet has so much energy.

Talk later, Harold

A friend of mine called me one afternoon to ask me a question. "I know a young couple from our church where the husband just finished going through the exact same treatments you're about to go into. He had throat cancer, had the tonsillectomy, the whole thing.

"Just like you," she said. "Do you mind if I give him your phone number?"

"Not at all," I replied excitedly. "I would love to talk to him!"

The very next day Shane called me and I liked him immediately.

The guy sounded a lot like me. Full of energy, excited to share his story and empathetic all the same.

"I have to tell you," he began. "This was the hardest thing I've ever faced in my life. I don't know what things you've been through, but I hadn't been through anything like this."

He went on to describe how he had been diagnosed. Unlike me, he knew his tonsil was enlarged along with his left lymph gland and went to see the doctor immediately. His ENT did a fine needle biopsy, which is where the doctor jabs a needle into the desired area and draws out a sample of liquid, tissue or whatever for testing. That test came back negative for cancer. Everything pointed to this being nothing but a cyst of some sort so he went up for his tonsillectomy, came home and started recuperation. The tonsils would be sent off to pathology for testing, but no one expected anything new to be discovered. Following the same schedule I did, he had a follow-up appointment with his doctor after about four days to talk about the results of the surgery. Mine was done over the phone since we knew going in that it might be cancer and my ENT had already broken the news to my wife. Shane had no clue and went to the appointment alone.

He told me that when the doctor told him the tonsil removed was malignant it took a minute for what he had said to sink in. Then it hit like a ton of bricks. "I cried all the way home," he told me.

He began radiation treatments very soon after everything got started and commiserated with me about all the doctors and dentists appointments leading up to it. We laughed about how it seemed we spent at least one 'co-pay a day' for the first two weeks.

He had a rough time with his treatments. Many of the side effects they warned both of us about got him. Since he started radiation much sooner than I did after the tonsillectomy, his throat became very sore early on and made swallowing next to impossible. It didn't really matter much, though, because everything had begun to taste so nasty that he threw up almost every time he ate. "The last few weeks," he said, "I threw

up every day when there was nothing to throw up. I would just gag and heave and gag, it was horrible."

"There were days I would just cry on my wife's shoulder."

"Man," I said.

"It was so tough." But then he perked up, "But I'm through it! And you'll get through it, too. Then it's over and the cancer should be gone for good. This is a good kind to get if you have to get it."

"How much weight did you lose?" I asked him.

"Oh man! Thirty pounds and I only weigh 150 normally."

That floored me. I weigh about 155 and knew I couldn't lose thirty pounds. No way.

Then he told me about the hair loss. "I have this goofy looking bowl cut now," he laughed, "but I'm too skinny to shave my head because then I'd look even worse."

He told me how the radiation sort of erases any hair in a ring around your head and neck. I wouldn't even need to shave for a couple of months and it really would look like I took a razor in a nice straight line around the back of my head right about ear level. Just lovely. Not good stuff to hear when you're as vain as I am.

He also told me about how supportive everyone around was and that he would gladly drive me to any treatments, meet for lunch or something or just talk any time I wanted to. He didn't have anyone that had been through this to lean on and had thought often that he would help anyone he came across in the future. He was surprised the opportunity arrived so fast, was sorry for my news but was there for me. I thanked him repeatedly and knew we would talk often going forward. Knowing I had him there was a great comfort.

During this call I had been sitting in our kitchen in the corner. I clicked my cell phone off, leaned over and rested my elbows on my knees. Then I bent my head down to my hands. I was very still and thought I might cry, but I didn't. I just went through all that he had said. "Get ready," I thought. "Get tough."

Debbie walked into the kitchen and I looked up at her. I remember my voice being kind of shaky.

"This is going to be very hard," I said.

"I know."

We just smiled at each other and nodded.

CaringBridge entry for December 8, 2008

Had a quick post-op visit with my surgeon today. Dr. Doogie[1] said I'm doing great and can start being active and working fully again after our appointment on January 5th....

not until January 5th? ... my bad....

Actually, *Mom*, I am being careful by not lifting anything particularly heavy.

Still haven't heard yet when radiation will start, but Radiation Doc says not to worry, he'll call me.

_____

[1] Remember that TV show about the child doctor "Doogie Houser, MD"? Well this guy is the youngest looking doctor I've come across. Of course it has nothing to do with me getting older....

Journal

responses

So glad to hear about the lifting!!
Or, actually, lack thereof.
Will be thrilled to see you.
Lots of love, Mom

Ed, so glad to hear the good news.
Keep doing what they say, and you'll be doing a jig in no time. You're always in my prayers, my friend, keep up the good work.
Barb

Yes . . . not until January 5th!
But, then again, since when have you EVER stopped working/playing/making trouble just because you had a "little" operation/accident/life-changing event?
Love you bro, Donya

Ed and Deb,
Thanks for the update, you're certainly in our prayers,
and it's tough to be patient. . .as in "waiting."
Melissa

Dear Ed and Debbie –
Hope you had a nice Thanksgiving.
Seems like there's been a lull in the action, and I just wanted you both to know that I think of you every day.
My parents (who are not so great about getting online) also asked that I pass on their well wishes. They were happy, but not surprised, to know that Ed's wonderful sense of humor and loquaciousness are unaffected. My sister also sends her greetings and wishes for a speedy recovery.
Take care!
L&R, Blake

CaringBridge entry for December 19, 2008 7:37 am

Well, things have moved slowly, but moved nonetheless. I met with my ENT surgeon yesterday for the final post-op visit for my initial surgery. He said things look great inside my throat and felt like what he expected for the lymph node and surrounding tissues. Which is to say I've got another lump there all ready. The radiation is designed to take care of that, and I'm finally scheduled to start that on Monday.

I was going to start this week, but there was some other delay that I'll hear about today at my appointment where they'll also do "some more film" of me and run through the upcoming treatment program. The best news is I get to take four days off over Christmas, so Debbie and I are bolting up to Richmond to see our kids and grandkids, then up to Annapolis to visit a big chunk of my family that I haven't seen in awhile.

Thanks again for visiting this site. I re-read everyone's comments all the time and take a lot of comfort in the encouragement and jokes that y'all have sent.

Much love.

Ed

responses

Hey Ed,

Just read the update. Glad to hear there's a plan and you're moving forward. We think of you and pray for you and Debbie regularly. We'd love to see you two when you come to Richmond.

Looking forward to God doing great things in your lives!

Amy & Clark

Thanks for the update!

Glad to hear the radiation is due to start and that you will be able to have Christmas with your family.

Will Lauren and/or Scott be in Annapolis? Please give hugs from us to your mom and sibs and, of course, your kids. Have a wonderful time.

Love, Chuck and Ann

Ed and Debbie-

It's a different kind of Advent for you this year . . .

a different kind of waiting. We continue to trust the miracles of medicine and your good spirits and God's presence to take on the treatments and the healing that will follow. We'll count on some real hugs to add to the virtual hugs soon. Love y'all.

Lori & Terry

PS. We went to a Duke game Wednesday night. Those youngsters were smokin'!

Undoubtedly your excited antics and volume would have embarrassed us if we'd been sitting together!

The Mask

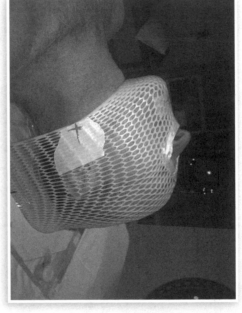

Just a tad Hannibalish, don't you think?

During one of my appointments at the cancer center,

I was told I was going to get my "mask."

I was also told the mask helped them precisely target the equipment so my cancer could be treated the most effective and efficient way possible. I said, "cool."

The tech had me lay on the table used by the MRI machine and asked me to stay perfectly still. I got on my back and she walked over to the other side of the room and started doing something in a sink. I could hear the water.

"This is going to feel wet and pretty warm, but it will cool down very quickly. Just stay still."

"Stay still. Got it."

She walked back over and I watched as she raised this dripping, white, plastic mesh thing above my face and asked me to close my eyes. I did and she planted it right down around my face, mashing it to the table. The white plastic meshed stretched tightly across my face and pulled my head down firmly to the table. I was startled a bit but remained calm as I heard her clicking bolts or something into the frame of the thing around my head to keep it in place. I also held my breath. I wasn't sure I could, or should, breathe through the thing so I just didn't. She had only said to stay still, so I was going to do that.

I thought of all the times I have had to crawl under the old, very low houses here in Manteo to repair joists, run a wire, pipe or whatever. And how just focusing on the task at hand and acting as if I had plenty of room around me would keep me from panicking. Some of those houses weren't more than sixteen inches off the ground and I would have to dig little trenches beneath each joist to get my body past it and on to the next one. Hauling jacks, tools, a flashlight and wires along the way. Every time something would crawl across the back of my neck or ankle I'd just start saying, "It's just a cricket. It's just a cricket."

I hadn't thought to take in a breath before she pushed the mask down and we were sitting there awhile with her saying, "It'll firm up in just a minute. Keep still." So I had to breathe and carefully. Didn't want to gasp so I just exhaled through my nose slowly, working to control that reflex and pleasantly found that air flowed no problem. Warm water dripped around my face and neck and the mask cooled quickly. I breathed in gently, not wanting to get any water up my nose. Success. After a few more seconds and some pulling on the mask above my

nose, she unbolted it and lifted it off the table. It was sort of cool looking - a screen that was now stretched and shaped exactly like my face except for the three inch long and very pointy nose.

"I pull the nose up like this because it would dry too tight to your face and wouldn't be comfortable during treatments. Most times we cut the nose out anyways and tape the edges up."

She looked it over and decided something wasn't quite right with it. It hadn't hardened enough before she lifted it off of me and had sagged on one side.

"Well, we'll just do another one real quick. Lay back."

"And we use this during the treatments?"

"Yes, today we'll do an MRI of you with this on, along with some marking dots on the mask. This way you will be in the exact same position for the radiation treatments. We can target the areas with varying degrees of radiation right down to the millimeter with this thing."

"And how long do treatments last?" Read that, "how long will I have to be strapped by my face to the table?" No, I wasn't looking forward to it.

"That depends on your program. Your doctor will go over that with you when you come in for the final setup."

It turned out that I would be attached to the table for about half an hour each visit. During the treatment I would receive eight different doses of radiation from eight different positions on a 360 degree circle around my neck. That would count as one round of radiation. Get it?! Radiation Doc has a very dry sense of humor, he is truly very funny and when I said that he smiled benignly and said, "In a roundabout sort of way." There would be thirty-five of said "rounds." Five days a week for seven weeks.

Now the machine used to deliver the radiation doses is really slick. It looked to me like a typical x-ray machine except that the head could swivel all the way around a table in front of it that lifted up off the floor to make room for treatments that came up from behind the patient. At each of the eight points that would be used to treat me, a different brass colored metal filter would be placed into the head of the machine. These looked to be blocks about six inches across, four inches wide and about three inches deep. They had used some sort of flo-jet type tool to carve out intricate reliefs into each block that would determine the amount of radiation I would receive. The thicker the block, the less radiation came through. It surprised me to see the myriad of depressions and stalactites in each one because it seemed weird to me that one square millimeter of my throat needed a dose of x radiation and the one right next to it only needed (x-5). What was even more surprising was that I actually used algebraic formulas while I thought about the blocks! My math teachers would have been so proud.

I would get one additional dose of radiation during my treatments to my supraclavical region. That's the area above the chest right along your collar bone. And this block was sort of silver instead of brass. Plus, it just had an odd, oblong shape cut out of it completely.

"How come this one is different?" I asked another tech.

He replied, "The silver one is sort of an off/on filter. If there is metal there you get no radiation. Where there's no metal, you get ALL the radiation."

"Sweet. How many doses with that one?"

He checked the chart and said, "20-five and we'll move it up and down your torso half an inch to blur in the treatment."

"And what's that one do for me?"

"This will kill your lymph nodes along your collar bone. They're the next ones down the line from your neck, so if you have any roaming cancer cells that didn't show up on the PET scan, we'll get them here."

"Yippee kayaa."

He laughed.

Each dose would last somewhere between a few seconds up to over thirty-five seconds. It all depended on the angle of attack and the filter used. I was impressed with the complexity of this approach and the obvious amount of work that went into developing it. I was beginning to think about how much research, trial, error, love, money, celebration and suffering had gone into the room I was sitting in.

I thought, "thank you everybody and thank you God".

Thirty-five and 20-five. Let's get it on!

CaringBridge entry for December 19, 2008 7:33 pm

I got a tattoo today.

No, really. A real tattoo!

Sure, it's only about the size of a pinhead, but now Scott (who's sort of covered in ink) and I'll have stuff to compare when he visits in January.

The dot is there on my chest to line up the equipment used for the radiation treatments. Get this: I have to lie perfectly still — perfectly still — for half an hour! I had no idea the treatments were going to be this tough. Of course that mask that straps my face down helps.

Today I kind of fell asleep on the table while they were getting everything ready, and the tech came in and asked me if I had moved.

"I don't think so. . . I was kind of asleep."

"Well, you're off about a millimeter up here."

Terrific, now I can't even catch a nap while I'm tied down.

responses

I'll have to tell all my friends who think I should be strapped down -- that it doesn't work! <:)

Here we are so close to Christmas, my favorite time of year.

As I think of all the close family members that are gone now -- its just Jeff and I now -- our friends become so much more important to us -- even those we don't see very often --

you and Debbie have touched our hearts and left such a lasting impression on us both. I'm so thankful to have the opportunity to tell you both that. Even if it means you had to be strapped to a table with duct tape to make it possible <:)

Have a beautiful Christmas. Jeff has a wonderful Christmas CD we would love to send to you both; pop your address to me in an email so we can send it out right away. Can't remember if we gave it to you already or not?

It was so cold the other night we actually had a very rare hail storm -- I saw all the white pebbles on the ground and thought we had had some type of toxic spill in our neighborhood -- took me a minute....

MERRY CHRISTMAS AND A HAPPY NEW YEAR!!

Jo Dee & Jeff

Ed, come on --- perfectly still for ANY length of time?

Lots of love, Mom

COMPLETELY STILL FOR 30 FULL MINUTES!!!!!!!!!!

Well Ed, I'm glad that I know for a fact that miracles happen.

Love you!!! We got the visa!!! We leave on Sunday!!!!
We are actually going to be in the States for a while!!!!
HAPPY DANCE HAPPY DANCE HAPPY DANCE -- I get to hug you and Debbie!!!
Oh, I picked up something for your grandkids...hee hee hee.
Love you both more than salt
(do you remember the children's story?).

Donya

Ed:

We have not seen each other in at least 15 years, and I hope your treatment is going well.

There is little doubt in my mind that you will come out of this little bump in the road with flying colors. I would expect nothing less from you. I will be thinking about you and your treatment and hope to see you at some point in the future. We are moving to Tampa in summer 2009. Currently I am in Kuwait. As somebody said once, "doing good ain't got no end." Still trying to do good for Uncle Sam. So, take care and have a good Christmas. Only good thoughts about you and beating the beast.

Mike

CaringBridge entry for December 22, 2008

All right! One down, 34 to go.

My first radiation treatment only took about 20 minutes and was just like they said it would be: uneventful. I was even able to stay still. The techs told me that in a couple of weeks I'll be asking them to boost the power level on the contraption because I won't be feeling anything at all. Shortly after that things will NOT feel like nothing is happening.

I've heard from a couple of people just recently who had friends or family that recently went through this treatment for throat cancer and felt almost no side effects at all. That would be sweet.

I added a couple of pictures of the first treatment so y'all could see this mask I've been talking about. Check 'em out!

responses

Ed, so glad to hear the treatments are going well, and that you will be able to start working again soon. I think about you every day. A local friend of mine, our same age, was diagnosed with colon cancer and is undergoing radiation and chemo, and he's responding well also.

I'm reminded of how thankful everyone should be who enjoys good health.

Your positive attitude is motivating to me and many others. Thanks!

Have a very Merry Christmas, Tom & Dorothy

Okay Ed, that mask is really something.

All you need is a hatchet, chainsaw or big knife and the picture is complete!

I can already hear some oneliners! If you do it right, you can be the one glowing at the top of the tree. Have a Merry Christmas and see you in the New Year.

Sheila

Ed, the picture of you with the mask on is truly a keeper. I can only imagine how very difficult it must be for you to remain still and not talk for 20 minutes.

I don't think I have ever seen you remain still for 20 seconds or quiet for 10 seconds

during the entire time we have known you. We are wishing you the best and hope you and your family has a wonderful Christmas.

Ray & Karen

Dude...that mask is crazy looking!

I am glad everything went well today. I'll keep my fingers crossed that every treatment goes as quickly and uneventfully as this one! See you and Mom in 2 days.

Love Us, Amy

Oh Ed, I am sorry to hear that you have cancer...you are definitely in my thoughts and prayers... I am glad Facebook exists to catch up with old classmates.

I am all too familiar with this website, my friends' son has ALS (leukemia) and I follow his updates as well. **Thanks for including me in your therapy and progress...I will be following you.**

Have a blessed Christmas! Ellen

Jeff and I are sending you both huge hugs for Christmas! We are so blessed to be here on this Earth at this special time. I'm listening to my favorite Christmas CD right now (wonder who?), finishing up at work and getting ready to go out with Jeff for our annual "see the lights in SF" walk. We went ice skating last week in Union Square -- I can't believe I didn't fall down! We have dinner with friends for Christmas -- we get two dinners! How special is that?!

Get some whey protein powder kiddo and start having banana shakes --

keep your potassium level up -- try EmergenC packets too!
Hugs to all and enjoy your family & friends! MERRY CHRISTMAS EVERYONE!

Jeff & Jo Dee

CaringBridge entry for December 23, 2008

Day two is done and I just had another monster lunch. Gotta keep eatin while the eatin is good, so to speak. The techs are great and move through things very quickly and obviously enjoy their work. Nice to have Christmas music playing along while I'm counting the length of each dose of radiation.

I'm not sure if I'll have enough radiation in me to glow in time to be the star on the Christmas tree, but maybe I could be the ball dropping on New Year's. Probably not. It's supposed to take a few weeks for the radiation to build up enough for me to feel it.

I've got one more treatment tomorrow, and then I'll head up to Richmond to have Christmas with all the kids. Of course I have to hang a couple of shelves first at Hilary's place.

"You're coming up here, Dad; can't you bring your drill and stuff?"

Of course I can, and I'm glad to do it.

Merry Christmas everyone!!

responses

Ed and Deb,

You are in our prayers as we know this week kicks it all off....

Glad to hear all going as scheduled in time for you to get to Richmond and enjoy family and food. If we do not see you the 24th, wishing you both safe travels and wonderful time away.

Have drill will travel . . .

Melissa & John

Ed, glad to hear all is going well so far. You're in our prayers every day.

Judy and I hope that your visit to Richmond goes well and brings you both peace and happiness visiting your family and friends.

Judy will send you a letter via snail mail since she is not too up on on-line email. Merry Christmas to both you and Debbie. We will be thinking about you.

Butch and Judy

Hey Ed — Just read the update from the 23rd.

Love your sense of humor!

We're down in NC visiting Sandra, Jerry, Jody and Jordan. How long will you guys be in VA? Hope you and the family had a very Merry Christmas. We'll be praying and of course looking for new updates on your progress. Love you guys!

Amy

Ed, we think about you a lot and hope for the best.

We say a prayer for your recovery every time we think of you.

I think about the fun we had doing "Little Shop..." and what a great job you did in that play. You helped me a lot with the directing because of your suggestions.

Hope to see you on stage again soon.

Lots of love,

Jerry and Joan

CaringBridge entry for December 29, 2008

The fourth treatment is in the books. Thirty-one to go. So far I feel pretty good except for a little bit of dry mouth. No big deal as long as I'm not trying to eat cookies. I currently weigh 162, which is an all time high for me, and I'm still trying to pile in the calories while I can. I'm doing that as balanced as I can without going nuts in tracking everything, but protein drinks several times a day along with carbs, etc.

I don't know if I've mentioned the fluoride treatments I do every day now. I got these rubbery trays made that fit my teeth to perfection and hold the fluoride against my teeth for a couple of minutes every night. This is supposed to help protect my teeth from all the radiation. Apparently cavities are one of those no-extra-cost throw-ins I get with the treatments. Until, of course, I go to my dentist again.

The toughest thing right now is trying to balance work and keeping folks happy. Difficult enough to do when I'm moving at full speed with a full day . . . but all in all things are going very well.

responses

Hi Ed, glad to hear you're moving right along. Hope you had a good Christmas with your family. I have you in my prayers and hope you keep on plugging. Hope to see you soon.

Take care and remember there are oodles of people who care about you.

Barb

Hi Ed & Debbie,

Glad to hear that you are doing well. If you get in a jam call Jerry, maybe he can help you out.

We are praying for you and brought you up in church for prayer.

Got a note from Amy just before Christmas. Glad you got to visit your family at Christmas. We love you and hope everything continues to go well.

Sandra

Hey Ed,

It was great to see you! You are not glowing at all!!

I am glad to get these updates and I am impressed with all that you and Debbie are doing.

I love you much!!!

xoxoxo, Lauren

Hello Ed and Deb!

Great to hear that things are plugging along, and

I'm glad to hear that you're keeping your spirits up.

I just wanted to drop by and say hello, and that I am thinking of you two. I hope y'all had a great holiday season.

Best, Colin

Hello guys,

Glad that ya'll had a good holiday and got to see the family. Ed, your attitude is wonderful. Just to let you know that ya'll have been in my thoughts and prayers.

Ed, just let me know when you want more brownies.

Happy New Year.

Jonta

I've said it a thousand times throughout this process, "I've got it so easy."

But that didn't keep me from whining about balancing work and getting through treatments.

Not long ago the closest place to the Outer Banks for radiation treatments was up in Chesapeake, Virginia. At best that was about an hour and half drive just to get there. If your treatments were being done by the oncology group in Norfolk during the summer months and your appointment was set for some time horrendous like 9 a.m. then you had to deal with summer beach traffic and daily commuter traffic in Virginia. Say goodbye to an entire day easy! And those appointments would have been daily, that's right daily, just like mine. Five days a week. Many times people tried to stay with relatives nearby the treatment center, or rented extended stay rooms if they could afford it. However, more often than not, people drove up each day they had treatment.

And that commute lead to lost jobs, incomes and family savings in

ED... IT WAS **MALIGNANT.**

the process.

To be fair, the Cancer Center pretty much allowed me to pick my appointment time. I decided to set it just before lunch so I had time to get everything rolling in the morning, then break for a "long lunch." Also, I could call into my guys and pick up anything they needed on my way back in from treatment. More often than not, I really didn't get much of a lunch. I would get home and suck down a bowl or two of soup then run right back out to get to the job site again.

In one of my many conversations with my Cancer Compadre, I brought up how tough it was to keep pace with everything when my day was cut by a third by having to go over to the beach for radiation. He understood and said he had to rearrange his day to start the work he would do out of the office right after going to treatments.

"But my customers were great, man," he'd say. "They were very under-standing and worked with my schedule."

"Yeah," I replied, "mine are saying all the right things, too, but I know they really want these jobs fixed right and fixed quickly. Maybe I'm just putting too much pressure on myself, but I swear I hear it in their voices when they ask how long something is going to take."

"Dude!" he exclaimed. "When it comes to handling customers who need something done pronto, you've got the ultimate playing card. The "C" card!"

I just laughed.

"I've never had to even say the word, man," he went on. "I just shrug and say, 'I'll get to it as fast as I can . . .'" his voice trailing off pathetically.

"You're horrible!" I chided.

"Your customers really do understand, Ed," he counseled me. "Just be straight about what you can and can't do and they'll be fine with it."

Great advice. I took it and I never heard anyone express anything but care and understanding. In fact more often than not they were surprised I got to things as fast as I did.

I tried the "C" card a lot at home, though.

Didn't get anywhere with it at all. If my wife and I were watching TV and I wanted another glass of water or something I'd ask her to get it and she'd just stare at me dumbfounded. I would look forlornly back at her and hold up my hand in the shape of a "C". She would hold up her hand with the middle finger extended.

A love was never truer.

CaringBridge entry for January 3, 2009

Well, two weeks of treatments are behind me and I still feel pretty good. The holidays were great, especially getting to see so much of my family. My dad and step-mom just left after visiting us from Colorado to bring in the New Year with us, which was great! Went to bed on New Year's Eve around 9 p.m. and woke up the next morning around 9 a.m. Perfect.

We also watched a ton of football, including Virginia Tech finishing STRONG with a win in the Orange Bowl. Hokie Hi!

The dry mouth continues, the weird sensation of something in the back of my throat hangs around, and that weird taste in my mouth seems to be here for good. So I'm pretty much focusing on March when I should be back to normal. Which is . . . what exactly?

responses

Good to see you yesterday as you drove by our house (maybe on the way to yours?).

Interesting that I was just thinking about you (a lot) today and when I checked e-mail, there you were!

So glad for the update, to know of your family's visit, that two weeks are behind you (as are the holidays) and things are going okay. Know you will be glad when it is all said and done! It was really good news to hear that you slept from 9-9 for a Happy New Year!! Hope to see you tomorrow at church. (Reminder: We are only a phone call away.)

Susan and Joe

Ed,

Was thinking of you this glorious sunny day and wondered how you're feeling.

Two weeks is a long period ...and is now behind you! Use the holidays with family AND the Hokie win as a springboard for these next few weeks.

We continue to send good thoughts and prayers your way.

Meliss and John

Hi Kids!

Good to hear you are able to get some rest and that you continue to focus on the positive -- as usual! I've got a beautiful fire going and our Christmas tree is all lit up -- dogs sleeping everywhere (3) and Jeff still asleep. One of my favorite times of the day. **It's SO good to keep up with you and hear how you are doing.**

Big hugs coming your way... Luv, Jo Dee

Hi, y'all don't know me but I'm an old friend of Donya & Phil from their Arizona days.

I got a prayer request from her right after the cancer was found, so we've (First Baptist~Sierra Vista) been praying for awhile :)

I'm so glad to have this site to be able stay current with your situation.

In His Love, Praying, Janne

Hi Ed,

I always find that your journal entries cheer ME up.

I am glad that you are maintaining your positive attitude and unique sense of humor. Remember to call on us if you need anything while Debbie is in Wilmington this week. SO many people in the shag club ask about you every time we have a get together. They are thinking of you and remembering you in their prayers.

Love you loads, Sandy and Jeff

Hey Deb, Hey Ed,

Thanks for keeping us posted, and I agree with Sandy: Reading your news brings a smile to my bearded mug as well. The fam, both immediate and extended, had a good time recalling some of our finer days in the way back. Most vividly was our dancing at my folks' wedding 27 years ago. Where did the time go? My parents say hey too, and their prayers are with all o' y'all. Otherwise, the only news on this end is that we're all preparing to go home for the inauguration. I'm going to do my part to bring this guy in right. I hope to have pictures to share with you. **Stay strong and patient. The time will pass quickly.**

Dwayne

As an Air Force brat, I grew up never thinking about medical insurance or expenses.

We had the IDs, we had the coverage.

Throughout my adult life I have always worked for companies that offered health insurance. While I was aware of the costs to me for the insurance, I never worried or thought about any major medical expenses because of the low deductibles and low out of pocket caps I always selected and could always afford. When Debbie and I both became self-employed we began to get an education in the costs of personal insurance policies.

Now, Debbie has some good experience in HR as a manager and knew very well the ins and outs of health insurances and did a great deal of research when we settled on our insurer and policy. The first year we had purchased our own policies we were able to have coverage very comparable to the kind we were used to as part of the group plans we once had, although we were paying much more for it. Not

only were we now responsible for 100% of the premiums, but those premiums were also higher than discounted group rates. We knew this would be the case going in and were resigned to the fact that it was just a cost we had to bear.

However, with each passing year, even though we were both very healthy people, our premiums steadily increased. With each increase, we had to make adjustments to take on higher deductibles and risk higher out of pocket expenses. And even with those concessions our monthly cost kept going up.

So when I was diagnosed with cancer, while we had "good" insurance, we both knew this was going to be a huge challenge financially. We also learned something about those out of pocket caps mentioned in the policies. They're really not caps! Things like a co-pay for doctor visits and prescriptions must always be paid by us. The caps apply to the actual bills; where initially we would be responsible for 30% until we reached that cap. So every time I had to see a doctor, get a test done or fill a prescription, I had to pay. It seemed like fifty bucks was going on the card daily.

With the economy in the toilet, contractors and handymen starving all around us, it made for a pretty scary proposition. However, both Debbie and I were fortunate to continue to acquire new customers and line up jobs. The real life saver was Debbie's business. A new client seemed to appear on the horizon every time another was wrapping up and since I had to hire people to do much of my work, her income was really all we had.

The downside to that was all of her business was showing up way off in Wilmington, NC. Neither one of us wanted to be apart during this, but what has to be has to be. It was an added stress but one we knew we could handle simply because we had to handle it.

Just after I was diagnosed, Debbie had the foresight to open up an equity line on our house. One thing we did have was plenty of equity, so if things got too bad income-wise we could still stay ahead of our bills. Not the best alternative, but not a bad one either.

Staying on top of a business is always a challenge. Making sure the jobs get done properly, keeping control of costs and working to keep new business coming in is just the beginning. Back end work, like

accounting functions, is constant. Trying to do all that when one key employee is operating at two-thirds speed and the other is out of town almost five days a week is serious work. Debbie did an amazing job carrying so much of the weight and together we kept above water.

But staying above water doesn't mean it was cheap or painless. My out of pocket medical expenses for November and December hit $6,800. Not a huge number when compared to the total costs of my treatments and everyone has heard medical bankruptcy horror stories, but it's still a lot of cash. Can you write a check for $6,800 right now? Not many people can.

Once again, because of our good fortune and ability to afford health insurance, we have it better than many others.

However, that could change.

And probably will.

August is renewal time and I'm guessing my rates will go up. We've looked at alternatives already, but there haven't been any affordable ones.

Being able to have health insurance, like knowing whether or not these treatments worked, wouldn't be known until later in the year.

One more thing that weighs on the mind of a cancer patient.

Other than that first night after the tonsillectomy, every piece of news I'd gotten was pretty good. As doctors talked to me about my prognosis, treatment program, and even the side effects I became more and more optimistic about how this was all going to go.

And that's when I started calling what I had "Cancer Lite."

I mean, really. How many illnesses are out there where the treatment is going to last about two months and then you're cured? Plenty.

"But you've got cancer," someone would say.

"And I won't in about 60 days," would be my reply.

"It's great to have such a positive attitude," my Dad told me, "but you don't have Cancer Lite."

"A large portion of my attitude is based on what every doctor is telling me about this," I assured him, "and as far as cancers go,; this is Cancer Lite."

One of the things I noticed right away after being diagnosed was how acutely aware I was of other people in my community who were suffering with cancer. I've always heard the words, said things like "man, that's lousy," prayed for them but then that was kind of it. Now all of a

ED... IT WAS **MALIGNANT.**

sudden I have almost a physical sensation of understanding. I can feel the queasiness of their treatments, the embarrassment of the physical changes like hair loss and peeley, blotchy skin. There's a connection. And immediately I feel guilty.

Because mine is going to be over pretty quickly.

If someone dealing with pancreatic cancer were to hear me complain, I would feel like crap. I've got a friend in my church who has been battling a cancer for years! And he doesn't have the motivational phrases coming from doctors like, "eight weeks of treatments and you should be good to go!"

As I went through this process I wanted to remain respectful of those who were facing a much more difficult challenge. I wasn't sure what I could offer those people after this was over for me, but I was going to keep my eyes wide open for those opportunities. The more in touch I am with what happens to me, the more in touch I can be for them. Having it this easy means I owe them something even if it is just my love, respect and admiration.

Other groups I owe for helping to make this Cancer Lite are all the scientists, doctors, patients and patrons who have contributed to the state of cancer treatment today.

Looking at the machine that treats me, those brass-looking blocks, the computer program tied in with a digital MRI of my skull and upper body is a tangible representation of who knows how many hours of hard work by who knows how many individuals to develop and construct. And try to imagine the financial cost of those hours. Now when I hear the budget numbers for research on TV for certain projects, my response is almost always, "Is that all they've got to work with? How can they afford to operate?"

And the patients.

Oh man.

You know those adorable little side effects I mentioned regarding teeth and jawbones? A friend of mine's mother went through head and neck radiation treatment about 20 years ago and is still having surgeries on her jaw to relieve pain and replace dead and decaying bone. 20 years later! Because of what doctors and scientists have learned since then regarding radiation dosage and delivery, I have virtually no chance of that happening. I am benefiting from the physical and emotional toll others have paid.

I owe them.

I've got it so easy.

Thank you, God.

CaringBridge entry for January 6, 2009

I was on my way to treatment today when they called and said the machine was down. They can treat with electrons, but not photons, and of course my treatment is done with photons. I knew that.

(My wife just raised one eyebrow.)

The Cancer Center hooked me up with some cool lotion for the dry spots showing up on my red neck. Yep, now it's official . . . as if the pickup truck wasn't enough.

responses

...humor really does seem to be the best medicine in your case, Ed!

Keep up the positive attitude, you remain in my prayers.

Mark

Dear Ed and Debbie,

So glad you still have that great sense of humor, Ed. Having that positive attitude will get you through this. I hope Debbie can survive all this. **Hope the New Year will be a better one for both of you.** You have a tough road ahead of you, but with all your friends and prayers, you will make it.

Love and lots of hugs for both of you,

Karen

Hey Ed & Debbie,

Thanks for the updates. I love reading them . . . they always make me smile. . . which seems backward.

Shouldn't we be encouraging you in some way?? I'm just glad to hear positive news and look forward to even greater things! Hope your Christmas and New Year's were nice.

Love- Amy & Clark

Never lose your sense of humor!!! You make me laugh and smile!!

Thanks and love,
Janet and Wayne

Redneck huh? Well, you do sort of look like the stand-up comic that does those jokes....

We all love him. I hope you are still feeling good.

Love you Bro, Donya

Hey Ed,

You know we all love rednecks... "Git 'er done." But maybe it's just a "reddish neck"? Let me check my thesaurus...page flip, page flip, page flip...oh, okay, try scarlet neck, crimson neck, cardinal neck (like VA state bird), ruby-colored neck, flaming neck (scratch that...well, don't "scratch," but you know what I mean). Oh, here's a good one: "ruddy neck." Titian and vermillion sound pretty, but I really don't know what they mean.

Oh, here's a good one: "white zinfandel neck!"

You could ignore the neck and go for "full body blush."

Love ya, man. Stay strong!

Dwayne

CaringBridge entry for January 9, 2009

Well, I'm officially one-third the way done with the treatments! 12 down, 23 to go.

Along with that are those side effects they were telling me about. My ruddy neck (I liked that one, too, Dr.) is now becoming a scabby neck, so I'm hitting it with hydrocortisone two to three times a day. Definitely helps with the itching. I'm also gagging quite a bit more. Not that I did it much before come to think of it, but most every morning I get close to losing my breakfast. The smell of milk doesn't help either. I think I'm done with that. Radiation Doc says that's pretty much universal: Milk tastes rancid on radiation to the throat. The saliva I still have tastes like I'm sucking on pennies, so pretty much everything has that extra seasoning on it. Different, but not horrible. But the lack of decent saliva makes it just about impossible to chew anything. So I'm on to soups!

Still only down two pounds since I started, but I can see keeping weight on is going to be pretty difficult, especially since I still work every day. For the most part my energy is good, but I hit moments where I really want a nap. But 20 minutes of one seems to do the trick, and I'm off and running again. The guys who work for me kind of shake their heads because they thought I was going to slow down. I tell them I will, but they might not notice it. They do notice my imitation of a cat hacking up a hairball, though, and it kind of creeps them out.

Makes my eyes water.

responses

Don't slow down! The earth is on its current axis due to the energy you two emit -- we would all fall off if you slowed down!

You are getting there -- one day at a time and doing great. Jeff and I are off to the Hot Springs this weekend -- can't wait to soak in those mineral waters and relax.

Have a great weekend -- and be glad you don't live in Oakland!

HUGS!!

Jo Dee & Jeff

Ed,

Glad to hear you are hanging in there during the treatments. I cannot imagine you letting something like this slow you down. Wish I was there to help you out during your 20-minute naps.

I need to pay you back for all the times you recharged me.

Best wishes, you are still in my prayers.

David

Hey Ed,

Thanks for the visual. Hacking up furballs! **Do we have to start counting the cats in the neighborhood?**

Glad you're getting thru the treatments. If soups are it, try good hearty ones. I make a mean beef vegetable soup. Let me know if that would interest you.

Love, Sheila

Meow...I mean, really....

Bert

I have not caught up to your site in a while.

I am glad to see that you are forging through.

Halfway done is a good thing.

Good as new by summer.

Thomas

Hang in there, Ed!! I saw Hilary yesterday and met her Aaron. He is sweet. Shawn and I are keeping you in our prayers. He is still going through his treatments as well with about 9 months to go. He is losing his hair now and he can identify with the taste in the mouth and tiredness.

It sounds like you are hanging in there quite well.

Hope it does not get much harder than this for you. You are in our thoughts!

Love....Laura and Shawn

You slow is probably everyone else moving fast!!!

Much love.

Myrna

CaringBridge entry for January 12, 2009

Thirteen down.

Radiation Doc and I had a talk last week about taste, dry mouth, etc. He said that many people find foods and drinks that actually taste normal, so I should grab three or four juices and see what works. So Saturday I got lucky and found out that just by sipping Gatorade the metallic taste was gone. The whole day! So I kept going into Sunday and for dinner had chicken, mashed potatoes and green beans. All smothered in gravy. Saawweeeet! It didn't quite taste completely normal, but it was still really good.

So now I keep a "sippy cup," as the folks down at the building supply store call it, of Gatorade handy and life's pretty good! Had oatmeal with whole milk and a whey protein shake for breakfast. Only gagged once. Unfortunately, Debbie had just asked me a question, so she got the full cat-with-a-hairball performance.

"Are you going to be all right?"

"Oh yeah, no – ackph! – problem."

Just finished a big ol' bowl of chicken corn chowder and feel pretty damn decent. No nap today, we're tearing apart a bathroom, framing up a new wall and prepping for a custom tile shower I'll do later this week.

Thanks for all the notes! And if you haven't done it yet, read the guestbook entries. Guaranteed to make ya smile.

responses

I really enjoy your graphic descriptions.

Maybe you should take up writing.

Glad all is going well!

Love, Joyce

Ed, you are awesome!

OK, I know that busy hands keep your mind in a good place...but, really, a whole new bathroom?

I missed my meeting with Deb today because I came down with the 24-hr bug. Even Gatorade doesn't work! Hopefully, I will be able to eat a little rice tonight! And, hopefully by tomorrow I will be able to hold something down. I love you both and look forward to Spring when we can have a cookout over at the new house!

Bebe

Hey Bo! Glad to hear it only took Gatorade! So glad something has helped!

Proves that the more people who share info with each other, the more good is done all 'round!

Things going well here --- lots of prayers from Annapolis and Saint Anne's for you and Debbie.

Lots of love, Mom

So one glaring concern...

a daily dose of Gatorade was the "secret" ingredient in my fertility treatments...seriously.

I have the 5-year-old child to prove it. So don't be surprised if you notice a "growth" in your abdominal area.... :)

Kelli

HMMM...let's see, Gatorade and brownies. Wonder what they would taste like if I used the Gatorade instead of my secret ingredient.

Or I could use some hairball remedy.

LOL! I will send some more your way next week. You and Debbie are in my thoughts and prayer.

Love ya, Jonta

You're awesome, Ed. Love from here.

Giggles

ED... IT WAS **MALIGNANT.**

CaringBridge entry for January 13, 2009

So, Debbie and I were sitting on the couch last night, basking in the heat radiation off of my neck. It doesn't quite crackle as well as our fireplace, but it's just as toasty. I decide to lean back, lace my fingers behind my head and rub my thumbs up and down some. Because that's not really scratching. A minute later I return my hands to my lap, it started to feel like scratching, and Debbie says, "What's that on your hand?"

"That," I say as I look at my fingertips, "is my hair."

Sigh.

So things keep progressing according to plan. Which, overall, is a good thing. If my skin and hair look like this, the cancer cells are right there with 'em. Which means I should begin having trouble swallowing any time now. So I'll be eating and drinking as much as I can to keep up the weight as long as I can. Today I was at 157. Not too bad.

responses

A poem in honor of your hair:

Your neck is red
Your eyes are blue
If people don't like you bald
You have my permission to say, "SCREW YOU!"

That was my edited version ;0

Amy

Hi, Ed --

Well, at least your hair has a chance of growing back, post radiation treatment. **Mine seems to be fleeing my head even without any "photons" chasing it off. :)**

Love your sense of humor. Hang in there, and keep eating, big bro'!

Love, Blake

Hang in there, Ed (and Debbie). We follow your progress daily and continue to keep you in our thoughts and prayers. You certainly seem to be doing the right thing in keeping a positive outlook on your illness, as difficult as it would be at times. **We have enjoyed and appreciated your candor and sense of humor.**

Fondly, George and Linda

I'm glad to see you're keeping your sense of humor. **I think a good sense of humor is the best medicine for whatever ails you!!!**

You're in our thoughts and prayers!!!! Love ya!!!!

Ginny

Hang in there, bro. Protein shakes... *yummy.*

I'm sending you hugs! Love, Donya

Hi Ed, thanks for the amusing updates. Your sense of humor remains intact, thank God. Sorry to hear that you are now dealing with some of the unpleasant side effects of your treatments, **but like you mentioned, it's zapping the "bad guys."**

You are in our thoughts and prayers every day.

Love to you both, Sandy and Jeff

Hey Ed --

I've been trying to keep up to date with your notes...sounds like the humor gene is still active.... I, too, am sorry to hear that things are starting to get a bit more complicated. If I can offer one possible thought of solace...my older brother (don't know if you'll remember Steve) had radiation down where he sits.... **trust me (or him), having a peeling neck is not too bad.**

Keep your chin up...halfway there!

Ken

CaringBridge entry for January 16, 2009

I met with Radiation Doc yesterday, and it turns out that as of today I am over halfway done with my treatments! I'm at 36 gray, which refers to the number of centigray I've been exposed to so far. I was told today that is the unit by which radiation treatments are measured. My total treatment is set for 7000 or 70 gray. Class dismissed.

The last couple of days I've seen my gagging/choking sensation increase, I'm losing chunks of hair along the base of my neck and my red neck is looking a little more violet along with some lovely peeling. Also, when I put my fluoride trays in the other night, I was surprised by the sensation that I had put a small block of dry ice in there instead. I later learned that fluoride can become very painful on radiated teeth, so it's time to stop those treatments until later. Brushing is even a tad painful, but I'm not allowed to stop doing that. However, I might switch over to brushing with baking soda since that doesn't have fluoride in it. We'll see. I don't want to risk any teeth/mouth issues over the next month because they could become really serious. So a little pain now should help me avoid a lot later, and as my dad always says, "a little pain never hurt anybody" . . . not too far from the tree am I.

Energy is still good, which is nice because work has been demanding lately. Thankfully.

Keep it coming, God.

responses

Hi Ed,

Thanks so much for the continuing updates...your messages bring such a smile and laughter, too!! Thank you. **With all the gloom and doom we hear about each day, you bring a hint at sunshine and hope!!!**

Hang in there and know we love you and are thinking about you!

Love, Janet and Wayne

Sounds like your treatment is moving along as well as can be expected. Glad to here you have plenty of work also. Keep up the positive attitude.

"May the force continue to be with you." Sorry, my 8 year old is playing a Star Wars video game.

Miles and Christen

Hi Ed --

I laugh every time I read one of your updates. You absolutely crack me up through all of this. I am glad to see that you put such a positive spin on things. In fact, I think the funniest image I had in my head was Debbie's facial expression when you were hacking up hairballs at the kitchen table!!! If only I was a fly on the wall. Glad to hear you are halfway through!!

You are a trooper and a true inspiration to everyone!

Love, Tara, Jay, Noah and Ethan

Ed,

You exhibit two essential ingredients for a successful outcome: faith in God and a terrific sense of humor. I pray you will exercise them both to the max!

And you have that third, secret weapon -- Debbie.

Bert

I like what the last guy said.

You do exhibit a great deal of strength for this situation, not just in body, but in spirit too.

We continue to pray for your healing and the strength to continue to bear good fruit from this. We also pray for Debbie as she provides you with a constant reminder that you are loved. And thank God for Gatorade!

Kevin

Hi sweets, sorry to hear how awful it is -- even when we know what's coming 9- its still a shock when it arrives. And there can't be anything worse than having pain and ulcers in your mouth -- would any of the numbing medicines help? If you can't get rid of them, perhaps there is some kind of wash that would numb the pain? If you haven't already, you must begin watching as many funny movies and reading as many jokes as possible.

Laugh yourself silly young man!

Jeff and I are thinking of you and sending you love and laughs....

"The problem with jogging is that the ice falls out of your glass!" Martin Mull

Jo Dee

CaringBridge entry for January 20, 2009

Well, this weekend was a bit tough. I developed a bunch of little ulcers on and around my tongue, which looks to be Thrush. Two thoughts jumped to mind here: 1) I'm feeling down in the mouth, and 2) Athlete's foot in my mouth? How do you suppose that happened? What did I say this time?

I know, I know.

I gargled with peroxide for a couple of days, but that made my teeth hurt, so I switched to salt water. That made things hurt worse but seemed to clear up a bunch of 'em. Radiation Doc wrote me a prescription for an anti-fungal thingy and said I'll feel better tomorrow. Then he corrected himself and said that the pain from the sores would be better, but everything else will still be hanging around and getting worse.

So since I was in pain every time I swallowed, and nauseated from the taste in my mouth, I decided to skip down the hall when it was my turn for treatment. Figured they'd never seen that before. Got a nice smile and nod from an elderly gentleman waiting his turn.

In reading the guestbook comments, I wanted to say something about a couple of the more recent comments because while it's obviously noticeable I haven't really said it outright. So here goes: God told me once to trust Him. I do.

Skipping to radiation treatment? You are amazing, Ed.

My parents asked me to tell you that they send their love, support and prayers.

As for me, if I could take your physical pains on for myself, I would. And I know a lot of folks feel the same.

With love and respect, Blake

Ed you are just unbelievable.

Kudos to Debbie too for putting up with your bad jokes.

Hang in there and remember we all love you!!!!!!

Barb

Ed,

Love hearing from you, love the humor you put into your experiences.

This comes at a good time for me. Tomorrow I go through the bowel prep for the colonoscopy scheduled for Thursday. When I scheduled this thing a few weeks ago, I was all for it. Needs to be done. Now the closer I get, the more I wonder about my own reasoning. Did I really choose to do this of my own free will? Mental lapses, male bravado, not sure where this became a good idea, but personally hoping for about 10 more inches of snow. Best wishes. You're in our prayers, and thanks for the updates!

Dan

Ed,

I just love to read your updates. You make me laugh -- the thought of you skipping down the hall...hilarious! **What an inspiration you are to others.** God has blessed you with your positive attitude and zany sense of humor! And you use those gifts to bless others around you. You and Deb are continually in our prayers.

Love you guys-- Amy and Clark

We are not happy to hear about the undesirable effects of your treatment but are so inspired by your continued positive attitude.

What a "Tigger" you are, even in these difficult times!

Hope by the time we get back to Manteo, things will be looking better -- treatments/worst part almost over! You and Debbie are in our thought and prayers even as we are miles away, and so glad you keep us updated through this website--through the good and the not so good days.

What a comfort to know and be reminded that God really is good--all the time!

Susan and Joe

I love you, bro.

hug

Hang in there.

Donya

I mentioned many times in my journal how I loved reading the guestbook entries. That really, really, really is an understatement.

They meant the world to me.

L et's review where I was at that point.

I had this constant, as in it was never not there, sensation of a ball of thick gelatin in my throat urging me to puke at random moments. I had a vicious sunburn that ran from between my shoulder blades to the back of my neck right at ear level. The oozing skin meant my shirts would stick there some and inflict some epidural damage every time I got undressed or even turned suddenly. My hair was falling out, giving me that really nice, patchy, yep-I'm-going-through-radiation-for-cancer look. I couldn't trust anything I put in my mouth to taste the way it did the day before and most everything I ate made me nauseous. My gums were receding so everything hot or cold touching my teeth caused me to flinch and spit. My teeth were beginning to hurt so much that chewing those little pieces of chicken in Campbell's Soup was a chore. And

now I had about a dozen little sores along my tongue and sides of my mouth that hurt so much when I swallowed or spoke that it made my eyes water and thighs flex.

And all this was just going to get worse.

Right along with all that was the fact that I was home alone. Debbie had a ton of work, which was truly a good thing for us, but it did mean that I didn't have her there to give me hugs or hold my hand on the couch. She wasn't there in the mornings to share coffee, Sudoku and oatmeal. She wasn't there at lunch time to talk about the morning work and what was left to do for the day. She wasn't there to share dinner and watch Law & Order. She wasn't there to curl up with at night. We spoke on the phone several times a day, every day, but the physical distance posed an emotional challenge for me.

We both wanted to be together during this, but we both knew that we had to be apart if we wanted to come through it in one piece financially. We also knew that in just a few short months this would all be behind us and the hard parts would quickly fade and shrink in scale as life went on.

Those were some of the thoughts I used to motivate myself. And that in itself would keep me waking up early, letting the dog out, keeping the house clean (mostly), picking up the mail, taking out the trash and washing the dishes. The fact that I had people depending on me to fix things at their homes and others who depended on me for their employment, also helped to keep me moving. But if that we're all I had I know I would have become more somber, more robotic and eventually depressed to the point that I would not have even resembled the old Ed.

Thankfully, there was something else.

There were those guestbook entries on CaringBridge.

I would read them each morning then again at night to see who had "dropped by" and of course latch on to their encouragement.

I wrote the journal entry for January 20th after I had come home from work. I was tired, my mouth hurt like all get out but I had pulled out a nice bit of inspiration that day at treatment and I wanted to share it with everyone who was keeping up with me. As usual I read the guestbook entries first and immediately felt better.

First, I love it when I make people laugh. Even though it's them laughing, I get a real kick out of their joyful experience too. Second, while I think about the spiritual aspects of my life and my relationship with God a lot, I don't talk about it much. It was nice to see someone recognized my faith in my actions. I figured that was about as good a compliment as I could ever get.

So after reading the latest from the guestbook I wrote about my day. The bad, the good and the silly thing I did to pump myself up and everyone else there at the Cancer Center. I also mentioned the fact that I do trust God in all of this. I do draw strength from His love for me.

Then it was time to eat something. Geez, I did not want to do that. I had taken the first pills for the anti-thrush medicine I had gotten, but they hadn't started to work on those sores yet. Not impatient, am I? I heated some soup, used my lidocaine rinse and tried to eat. No dice. It just hurt too damn much, and I figured I could go one night without dinner. Instead, I kept to water, watched some TV and then went to bed. I didn't even brush my teeth. I kept the magic mouthwash next to the bed and used it several times during the night whenever I woke up from the pain.

The next morning started like usual. The coffee pot making bubbling sounds and the dog walking slowly across the floor toward our door, her toenails clicking along the hardwood floor. I got up, walked downstairs, let the dog out, raised the shades, went to the bathroom and came back upstairs to get dressed. I guess due to the pain and waking up alone again, I was feeling pretty sorry for myself. I needed some extra punch to get my mind right for the day, so I went back to our office and clicked on the computer. I had intended to scroll back and reread some of the funnier comments people had made, but saw Blake's latest entry right off the bat.

Blake was my Little Brother in my fraternity at college. We did a lot together and were very close friends. After I graduated from Virginia Tech, though, he transferred up to Maryland and finished school there. From that point we lost touch as our lives kept us going in different directions and in different places, but our friendship was always a constant. Whenever we did catch up it was like we hadn't been apart.

I smiled as I began reading his note to me and then I could hear his voice turn quiet and serious as he said if he could take on my physical pains he would and he knew that many other people would too. I swallowed hard, took in a long breath, paused, exhaled and then began to cry. Sitting there at that computer I felt his hand on my shoulder and could hear his voice. I knew if our roles were reversed I would have said the exact same thing and meant it just as much as he did. I looked up and down the computer screen at all the other names of friends and family and absorbed all of their encouraging remarks. The tears just dripped off of my nose and chin and I thought if anyone I knew was in this situation I would be willing take the pain from them as well. I wiped my face and sat up.

"Well, you've got the pain you'd willingly take, Ed," I thought to myself. "Now take it."

I went downstairs and set about eating as if nothing hurt and nothing tasted bad at all. I focused on Blake's words, thought about everyone who was out there waiting for my next journal entry and did what I knew I had to do to keep my strength and attitude up.

I ate. And when it hurt, I smiled and then just kept eating until the oatmeal, protein drink and Ensure were gone. When I was finished I rinsed with my magic mouthwash and relaxed as the pain subsided in my mouth. One more great breakfast in me and I was ready for another day above ground. I thought about Debbie and how at the moment I put the last empty glass down she'd say, "Good job, Ed, you're such a big boy!" That made me smile big and then I practically bounced out the door to my truck.

As I turned on the radio and jotted down my mileage in my calendar, I smiled to myself thinking of all of my wonderful friends and family then said out loud, "Thanks God."

CaringBridge entry for January 22, 2009

A quick update before I run off for my day:

The sores in my mouth may be coming from electrons being kicked off of the fillings in my teeth as opposed to being Thrush. Not good news because there isn't really much we can do about that. I do have a numbing mouth rinse I use before I eat and when I go to sleep, but it only works for about 10 minutes. Less if I'm eating.

So the routine is to rinse with salt water, use the mouth rinse, eat and then just keep moving as if nothing hurts. I've got one sore showing up near the tip of my tongue so now I talk sort of funny. Debbie says on the phone I sound like Charlie Brown's teacher.

I also threw up twice yesterday. Kind of strange since I never felt nauseous. Just sitting there watching TV and thought, "Start running, Ed, you're gonna puke." Radiation Doc says that can happen as my saliva thickens up. Just lovely.

It's not all bad, though. I actually feel better right after and I forget about my mouth pain.

I had to quit drinking Gatorade, though. Started to taste nasty and oily to me. This whole taste thing is a constantly moving target. As for the soups I eat, I avoid anything spicy and go for clear broth sort of stuff. A couple of steady items have been instant oatmeal and fried eggs. While neither one tastes "normal" to me, neither one tastes bad either.

And as of yesterday I'm only down to 153 pounds, so this mechanical eating is keeping me up somewhat.

Fourteen more treatments to go! :)

responses

So, you are losing your hair so your head will look like Charlie Brown, and now you sound like his teacher. We have seen you come home from work looking like Pigpen. I guess you will be on tap to do a one man show of "You're a Good Man Charlie Brown." Seriously, Ed, we think about you all the time, and our Sunday School class talks about and prays for you and Debbie. You are an inspiration for the way you are handling this difficult time, and know we love you and Debbie. **Maybe now is the time to try some foods you always swore you would never eat.**

Ed & Lynda

I just read your latest entry, Ed.

For what it's worth, your descriptions are reminding a lot of us that our daily aches & pains are "a walk in the park" compared to what you are going through.

Being a tried & true HOKIE though, we know you'll prevail.

Joe

Geez Ed,

Fourteen to go sounds like light at the end of this huge dark tunnel. THAT IS great news! Keep us posted on what tastes good and what doesn't. We might be able to come up with some compatible items. Great on the weight front! We're thinking and praying for you daily. **As you already know, you're not walking this alone.**

Melissa

CaringBridge entry for January 24, 2009

I went for my follow-up visit with my hematology oncologist yesterday. He's Chemo Doc. Very nice guy, and he confirmed my excellent prognosis. He doesn't think I'll see this cancer again.

Whoohoo!

He also kept looking at me and saying, "You're at 46 (gray)? You're at 46?!" He said I was the Poster Boy for head and neck radiation. Couldn't believe my energy level and how good I look.

I said, "Easy Doc. I'm married."

The mouth pain has subsided a bit with the medication and the laticane. I so have to learn how to spell that. Chicken soup sort of things taste pretty good, but I'm still switching between Gatorade, water and soda through the day to get by the gagging moments.

My hairline is getting really bowl cut looking in back, so today I'm cuttin' it off. Not that anyone will notice since hats seem to be a permanent part of me.

Thanks for all the support folks! I love ya!

responses

Hey, the news from the doctor sounds very encouraging!

I always suspected you would end up being the poster boy for something...just wasn't sure what. Ha ha!

Still praying.....
Bert

Roses are red
Violets are blue

There are things weirder than no hair and a red neck,
Like having a permed afro that's dyed blue.

Amy

Are you going bald or just buzzing it?
If bald, please send me pictures!!

lol. Love ya.
Hilary

Keep up the good work, Ed... and the great spirits!

Love, Betty & Mike

Hi Ed,

First, Happy New Year to you and Debbie!

Roger and I have been reading all of your updates and are thrilled to hear that you got such a good prognosis from the Docs! Long distance hugs from us both.

We hope to be in the OBX soon so we can give you some more hugs in person.

Oh, and Tucker wants to send a sloppy wet Labrador kiss to you both.

Love, Kathy and Roger

Yo Crazy Ed. Woohoo! Great news.

And hey, don't worry about that bald thing -- been there, doing that, and Kay still loves me.

Take care,
Steve & Kay

Hey Ed! Just got back from a Women's Retreat weekend (and you thought we never retreated!), and you are now being prayed for by even more Marylanders!!!!

Love you and Debbie, and send pix of shaved head when you can!!

I remember you before you had any hair on your head anyway.

Lots of love, Mom

CaringBridge entry for January 26, 2009

Just to clarify things, I only buzzed my hair. At least for now, since Radiation Doc said not to shave it because that millimeter of hair on my head would affect how my face is held in that mask they use to tie me to the table during treatment. (I'm no English Major but I think that qualifies as a run-on sentence.)

So I've got a nice, high neck line now. Got that Audrey Hepburn thing going . . . either that or Ernest's bowl cut. Pick one.

I asked today so I could share: I have 13 treatments left. I still weigh 155 pounds, and I'm still working all day like normal. Every time one of my guys wants to take a break, like during a bathroom demolition today, I just look at 'em, roll my eyes and say, "wusses."

Now that the mouth pain seems to be under control, I feel pretty good! Ate two big bowls of some chicken and dumplings a friend brought over because it tasted just like chicken and dumplings. That got me excited, so I grabbed a chocolate and bit into it. No dice. I'm not sure how to describe the taste because it didn't stay in my mouth all that long. Straight to the trash can.

Ah well, someday it'll be chocolate again and I'll pig out.

responses

Ed, you just let me know when chocolate is chocolate again, and
I promise lots of brownies just so you can pig out.

Jonta

So Ed, send the chocolate to Betty W or Karen M. Betty would just die screaming

OOOOMMMMYYYGODDDDD -- you threw away chocolate!!!!

Glad you are doing so well -- but knew you would -- you do everything well, or so Debbie says.....

Ray

Hey Ed,

Glad to hear you're doing well, taking everything is stride. You're such a trooper.

We have a good friend at church who went through everything you are going through right now.

He said he'd be more than willing to talk to you and compare horror stories, encourage you, etc. He's a great guy, little older than you, with a great story to tell. If you're interested in talking to him, I'll get you his number. Let me know.

We're still praying for you and look forward to more updates.

Take care--Clark & Amy

CaringBridge entry for January 29, 2009

Just a quick update this morning before I run off to work. I added a new picture of my bowl hair cut line and red neck. Very attractive I assure you.

Today will be the last treatment for my supra-clavicle area, so I think the burn on my upper back will begin to heal. And after Friday I have exactly two weeks left and I'll be done!

I've noticed that it bugs me that I still have my sense of smell. I walked by a Subway yesterday and thought, "That's what I'll have for lunch! No . . . wait . . . they don't make a steak & cheese on Italian bread with provolone soup in there, and it'll only taste like chunky motor oil anyways." Pizza smells really good, too. And in the grocery store, when I was in there to pick up some more fizzy water stuff (that's what I'm drinking now), I stopped and picked up a box of glazed donuts and inhaled deeply. Looked like a fruit loop, I'm sure.

So attractive.

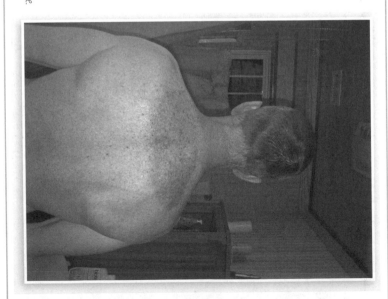

journal

responses

Hey, Ed!

It sounds like you're handling all this with great grit, strength and determination

—— not to mention a great sense of humor. I just wanted to add my own note of encourage-ment to you and Deb. You guys are in my prayers morning and night! Let me know if you need some snow sent down your way -- we got 16 inches last night. Today is balmy and sunny -- only 20 F however!

Mark

Hey Ed,

Just saw the new pictures. You now qualify for any SciFi movie out there with little make up needed! **No seriously, you look great!**

Your positive attitude and sense of humor are truly inspiring. I know so many people have been and are still praying for you, and that can only count in your favor.

Can't wait to see you again,

Sheila

Hey, Ed. We were looking at tile today at a local shop. The new manager is a guy who just moved from OBX...Jason. We asked if he knew you. He delightedly said yes and immediately started talking about what a nice guy you are. He talked about what a great voice you have, wondered if you had ever been on radio. We told him you sang and acted. He was not surprised. After we had swapped Ed fan club stories long enough, he said to tell you Hi.

Your fan club stretches a long, long way!

Glad you're getting close to being able to enjoy food going only one way!

Hugs to you and Debbie.

Lori

CaringBridge entry for January 31, 2009

Threw up again Thursday night.

You know chicken corn chowder doesn't change a whole lot between going down and coming back up. I thought about not sharing that, but this is my journal and it was something I noticed.

I've also noticed my face is getting tanned. But only from my cheekbones down. You remember that guy in the Fat Albert cartoon who wore his ski cap down over his face with eye holes cut out? That's my tan line. I've always enjoyed entertaining people, and now I can do it by just standing in line at the grocery store or bank.

Radiation Doc said I wrap up my treatments a week from Thursday! Now I only have nine to go. Which is good because my gums and throat feel pretty raw all the time now.

Nine to go.

Less than two weeks before I can start healing . . . hurry up clock . . . keep ticking.

responses

So glad the treatments will be done soon.

Love the new picture with your "sunburn."

I'm glad you haven't lost your sense of humor. Thank God for that. Can't wait till you're out with us Theater Of Dare people again. Hope to see you soon. Luv ya.

Barb

Ed --

I love Chicken Corn Chowder but sorry it "visited" you again. You have an amazing outlook and the best sense of humor -- I know it has served you well during this time.

Sounds like you are in the home stretch, and I am glad that things are progressing nicely.

Thinking of you and Debbie often!

Take care, Alice

Hi Ed (and Deb), just wanted to let you know that we're keeping our eyes on ya!

So proud and thankful for the example you are giving to us.

I'm sure that with your grit, faith and Deb's help, you will have much to share with us for many years to come! Love and prayers your way.

Danny

Great shots, Ed!

What's the grossest thing you've reproduced other than the chowder?

Thinkin' of you, bro...

Chris

Ed,

You probably won't be able to stomach this right now,

but once the treatments are over and you feel more like eating, try lots of cheesecake!

It should help you make up the deficit. I can gain 5 lbs. just looking at one!

Hang in there. You are in our thoughts a lot.

Kathy

CaringBridge entry for February 2, 2009

I looked at the bottle of my magic mouthwash and busted out laughing.

I now know how to actually spell lidocaine! Here I've been typing laticane knowing that it was probably wrong, but it was how it sounded when the folks at the Cancer Center said it. Gotta love the accent.

My brother came with me today to my treatment. He took some more pictures and saw the drama in person. Boring is an understatement.

"So you just lay there and it's done?"

"Yep."

"What do you feel when it's happening? What about right now that it's done?"

"Nothing. I don't feel anything right now. I won't notice anything more until later tonight."

"How anti-climactic."

And with that I only have eight more treatments to go. The mouth and throat pain keeps creeping up, so I've got more magic mouthwash to numb things when it gets bad. My weight is now right where it should be normally, so I expect I'll get a little skinnier over the next couple of weeks or try to squeeze in something new that's fattening and I can actually stomach.

responses

Hi, Ed. I was glad to hear that your brother has had a chance to visit. I'm sure that you all had a good time together despite what you are going through.

Thanks for the latest news. We do think of you OFTEN!

Love to all, Dan and Katherine

Ed and Debbie:

We keep up with you through your friends in Discovering the Depths class.

Remember how precious you are to us!

We pray for complete healing and for your spirits to be uplifted daily. God is strong and He is good! Love always.

Joan

Hey bro,

...seems like I only see you when we pass vehicles on the street, and I am blessed by your consistently bright smile and enthusiastic wave...

your grasp and witness to the world of the inner strength of faith found in Jesus is something the effects of lidocaine (or anything else) will never numb out!

Love ya, bro!

Major

Howdy,

Oddly, even in your struggle your true nature seems to rise to the surface, and that's beautiful because we LOVE your true nature. Keep keeping us posted. As for all of your friends, they all sound wonderful, and I'm glad there's so much LOVE in your life.

Dwayne

Hey!

True nature, huh? Do you remember the time I got braces? I was so worried about how I looked. I was a teenage girl. **And you, yes, you took one long look at me (I knew that my big brother would build up my confidence), and said, "What's different? You look uglier today than usual."** True nature. Actually I laughed, and whenever I think of that moment, I laugh. I really do like your true nature.

Love,
Your little sister
Lauren

CaringBridge entry for February 6, 2009

I love reading the guestbook part of this site before I sit down and write. It really lifts me up and gives me the encouragement I need to keep from just parking on the couch. I've known for a long time that the activities I choose to do affect my emotional state, and sitting around doing nothing makes me depressed. The fact that I can make other people smile just by being out and about is even more incentive to get up and just do my thing.

Not that I don't sit around and whine sometimes. Debbie will tell you that some evenings in front of the TV I'll just be pathetic. I guess I just need to complain sometimes about the pain, throwing up, etc. to get it out of my system, then I can move back to who I am by nature.

Which, apparently, is quite the stud.

Now, normally I don't make that claim except to my wife, and yes she does the eye roll thing, but Radiation Doc had a sit-down with me yesterday to explain what they normally see in head and neck radiation patients.

"Ed, do you know how many radiation patients keep working throughout their treatment?"

"(Head shake and shoulder shrug)"

"It's not quite zero percent."

"Sweet!"

"You're just bee-bopping (yes he actually said that) right through this."

Oh, one last thing: When the radiation techs come down to get me for my turn in the radiator, we all skip back down the hall together and laugh.

Five more treatments to go then I get to start healing up.

responses

Hi there! Well, I might be the only person on this list to have a bone to pick with you, young man!

Since you began this journey your positive "can do" attitude has ruined my ability to whine about how tough my life is!

No longer will a tired look get Jeff to cook dinner! No leaving work early anymore since I told my boss about you! In fact with Jeff's new "No excuse -- think about Ed" policy, I've even started working out again -- thanks for that! It's not enough that after meeting and working for Debbie, she improved my work ethic forever; now you've changed my personal life ethic!

Good grief! Now Jeff and I have a 5-year plan to spend more time at the lake house we always wanted. So on top of everything else I'm doing, I'm driving 3 hours up north on the weekends viewing houses and up to my eyeballs in loan paperwork...all because of you!

What's next? A marathon?

Jo Dee

Just a thought...when you're done with the treatments,

I'm thinking that with a wig and a blue checkered dress, you could audition for the lead in *The Wiz*.

No need to have wasted all that good practice skipping, right? Might as well be down the yellow brick road.

Bert

---

5 more!!!!!!!!!!!!!!!!!!!!!!!!!

Chris

Dear strong soul --

Today may not be one of those days you are thinking you are amazing, but take it from your fan club: You are amazing! Your current "almost there" status gives rise to new words to an old tune,

"And it's one, two, three more you're done with this ole ball game." Here's to the home run of no more treatments, no more cancer and

eating all the peanuts and popcorn and crackerjacks you want.

Hugs. Lots of them.

Lori

Hang in there, Ed! We're praying for you here in MisourAH! Go Tigers!

I always enjoy your commentary.

I guess your fingers don't hurt as much the talking.

Joyce

You are almost done, Ed!

I am sure that the rest of us would not even be on our feet, much less working.

I continue to be awed by your resiliency and positive attitude. Hang in there, bro'!

Love, Blake

ED... IT WAS **MALIGNANT.**

Ed,
All I have to say to you is you're awesome!!!!

Thank you for sharing so openly with all of us...
you're an inspiration!!!!! I look forward to your updates, not only to know how

you're doing, but also I know that you're going to say something to bring a smile to our faces!

We love you!!!

Ginny

5 more to go!!!!!!! OMG. You can do this.

Pound that broth, maaaan.

Scott

Be-bop-a-loola -- you're our inspiration
for positive thinking.

Keep on rockin' and rollin' -- only 5 more to go.

Anne and John

Ok...now you have me skipping and rolling my eyes...stud...hahhahahaa (:

The sign on your truck makes sense now... you're a "call" guy right?!

Proverbs 17:22a
A merry heart doeth good like a medicine.

Major

My truck. Hence the "call" guy joke.

CaringBridge entry for February 9, 2009

Well, this stuff is finally taking its toll on me.

The sores in my mouth are getting worse, and now it hurts to swallow even water. If I have things warmed up first, like my soups, then it's easier. I keep the lidocaine handy at all times because it really hurts to talk, and I seem to do that a lot. Go figure.

Of course by using the lido, I tend to slur my s's (pronounced "ES sez" unless I have the lidocaine, then I say "ESH shezh").

So I got my guys moving on the tile work for one bathroom remodel I have going and another guy touching up the paint at the house that got hit by the plane, then I parked on the couch. Had to be done, I'm afraid. Funny how the pain drains me so much, and the nausea and gagging didn't seem to faze me. But I've still eaten my regular meals so my body will have the energy to keep trying to heal itself.

Three to go.

responses

The good news: This, too, shall pass....
Bert

Our thoughts and prayers are always with you... hang in there!!!!
Lots of love to you and Debbie!!!!
Mark and Ginny

Almost there, bro! Then sweet relief!
Chris

Hi Ed,
I've been reading your journal entries regularly.

Sounds like you've had a few struggles, but your good attitude is keeping you going.
I know your silly wife keeps you in stitches as well. Tell her I said hello.

My best friend had 30+ radiation treatments after a double mastectomy and chemo. I don't think the radiation effects lasted all that long. It's been 3 years now and she's doing great. You've been an inspiration to me. Not sure I could handle what you've been going through with the upbeat attitude you have. Keep it up! It's almost over.

Vickie

3 more and the sores are worse! Those ***************** sores better not get in your way!!!!

3 more to go. 3 more to go.
Scott

Dear Ed,
You are in my thoughts and prayers. I just learned of your news and was so sorry to hear this. I have enjoyed reading your postings and your positive attitude is impressive. I

I'm so glad to read it's almost over.
Take care. Kelley

Hallelujah! 3 to go! Being a runner you'll remember what the coaches always say, **"Run it through. Don't stop at the finish line, but run through it."**

So keep up the skipping, and may God grant you a quick and thorough recovery!
Kevin

Hi Ed, Hang in there! Just a few now.
Your sense of humor is incredible, Ed, and made me laugh out loud. **I know you have licked this thing by now, but now comes the tough recovery.**
I pray the hydrocodone will help ease the pain.
Stay tough! Mark

CaringBridge entry for February 11, 2009

Didn't sleep much last night. The lidocaine lasts about 15 to 20 minutes, and that's about the longest I stayed asleep. So today after I skipped down the hall and got radiated, I talked to Radiation Doc about the pain.

"I need some hydrocodone, Demerol or maybe a really big rock to help me sleep."

"The rock has too many side effects. Let's go with the hydrocodone."

My Cancer Compadre, a guy here in town who went through the same treatments a couple of months before me, said he got to the point where swallowing water felt like swallowing razor blades. Mine is more like swallowing a piece of barbed wire. Sharp pain but only in a couple of spots in my throat. Yawning, however, is a different story.

The first time I did that last week, I was at home, which was good because I wasn't ready for it and cried. Now when I feel one coming on, I can try to hold my mouth just a little bit open and limit how much the throat stretches. So I kind of do this thing where I lift one leg and flinch, then my eyes only water a little bit. Debbie got to see that in the grocery store yesterday. Stupid involuntary responses.

Radiation Doc was going to put me on some sort of patch that would deliver the pain medicine consistently over time, but I said, "dude, I'm going to be over this a week from now, isn't a patch overkill?" He said he could give me a smaller dose but thought I would do better with the liquid hydrocodone and agreed that I don't really need to manage the pain 24/7.

So there's only one more trip for treatment. I've driven myself to every one of those and will again tomorrow. Seems to have gone by very quickly, but I know the side effects will be with me for at least a few months after the treatments stop. At least that's what they tell me. I'll see what I can do.

Thanks for all your support. It's been overwhelming and really helps me to keep on getting up and doing my thing each day. Keep praying for me, though. I've still got to find out how my jaw bone and teeth have done through all of this. Some of the lower teeth honestly don't look very good, but maybe they'll bounce back. I've been brushing like a good boy.

responses

Ed and Debbie -- I wrote this once but lost it before I sent it I think. One of your messages quoted some coach's advice to "run through it--get to the finish line and keep running!" That will help you, I hope. You'll breathe a sigh of relief after tomorrow for sure, but keep skipping through your healing time as well. We will certainly be "praying through" that with you.

Sorry the barbed wire has been so tough these last days, but here's hoping those barbs will melt away!

Your sense of humor has made us laugh -- the most recent example was to suggest a rock to ease the pain, foregoing it because of the side effects! You have evidently had great moral support from the medical staff along the way. We thank the Lord for that, too.

Love, Bob and Esther

Hey Ed, wow, almost there! I've been keeping up with your story and we've been praying all along the way. I told you I was looking forward to God doing great things, and although it's been a rough ride for you, it seems He really has blessed you...and continues to do so.

We'll keep praying.

Read Jeremiah 29:11, it's very encouraging.

Love you guys!
Amy & Clark

1 more!!!! Yay!!

I am praying for you. I love you very much. xoxoxo

Lauren

At times, the concern and enthusiasm for my well being would become quite humbling.

In addition to all the encouragement I got from the CaringBridge site, I received a ton of support first-hand. Everywhere I went, people would pat me on the back, tell me I look great and ask how things were going or what the latest news from the doctors was. They would also tell me stories. Share experiences they themselves had or those of friends or family members. I felt like the whole town was looking out for me.

Remember the mom and daughter who brought me the "Happy Birthday" balloons when I was first diagnosed? The mom saw me a week or so later and came up to tell me something that had happened a couple of days after the visit.

"My daughter and I were driving through town," she started with a big smile, "and I guess she saw you coming out of Food-O-Rama, but she suddenly shouted, "Mom look! There's Ed! He's a survivor!!"

We both laughed and traded "Isn't-that-cute's."

"She was just so excited to see you out and about, Ed. It made her day."

As I got in my truck, still grinning because I felt like I had a fan or something, I started to think about what that comment showed about her thoughts when she came and visited me in the first place. Immediately, I started to get choked up and was glad I was driving alone.

Here was this young girl who brought me balloons along with her mom because they heard I had cancer. The whole visit she laughed with me about the balloons, gave me big hugs and sat there on the couch smiling while we all hung out and talked for a few minutes. I remembered how nice a visit it was, how sweet she had been to bring me a gift and spend some time with me. Now I realized that she was under the impression that I was probably going to die and very soon. Even so, thinking the worst, she was there and supporting me. Kids can be amazingly courageous.

I see that girl at church and around town and I always make sure to give her a big smile and hug.

Along with the verbal support I got on a daily basis, I found that my mailbox had become a great friend of mine as well. At least a couple of times a week, almost daily the first couple of weeks after my diagnosis, I would receive cards and packages from all over the place. Friends or family sent their love and support in a way that let me hold it in my hand and keep it on my desk to look at again and again.

One evening I came home from work, walked in the front door and from there I could see that there was something very large on one of my kitchen chairs. As I walked closer and turned on lights I saw that it was a big piece of poster board made into a card that had a big, smiling sun drawn on it and hand prints and signatures of the children from my church along with the message, "Mr. Ed – Thinking of You."

There was also a monster bowl of spaghetti and another of a terrific tossed salad complete with ranch dressing. And here I was wondering what to do for dinner that night.

"Oh man..." I said aloud then just swallowed hard and wiped my eyes.

On another day I received a big pink heart card from the two children of my Carolina Fan Pharmacist, telling me to "feel better soon" and "we love you." He included two beers from a local brewery to be enjoyed when my taste buds came back. And I didn't even need a prescription for them.

Both of those cards are still up on my office wall today.

The local quilting club, The Teacup Quilters, brought me a gorgeous quilt to wrap up with on the couch and I received an incredibly soft and warm knitted shawl from my son-in-law's mom's church group in Williamsburg, Virginia. Both of these organizations provide these items to seriously ill people who come to their attention as a ministry. I guess it's no secret that cancer patients tend to get chilly as the weight starts coming off during treatment. Those gifts, along with two other shawls my mom made for me and my wife, got a serious workout through the winter and they will be cherished for a long time to come.

I was sent books by several folks. Not necessarily on any particular topic, just things they thought I might enjoy reading. I also got some cool CDs to listen to as part of a "redneck" theme gift I got to honor my radiation burn. I noticed something interesting while reading and listening: Not only did I enjoy the items sent for what they are, but I also got the sense that the givers of those gifts were right there with me as I enjoyed them.

And of course I got a couple of hats.

My mom made a really nice knitted one that felt great when I snuggled it on and my sister sent one from Brazil that was especially made to embarrass my kids. Simply awesome.

With each card or gift I got a distinct sense of comfort by knowing that these people were thinking of me. I wasn't alone in this and didn't need to be my only source of energy. There were people I could rely on and draw from. Moreover, they were letting me know that I was loved.

And knowing that one is loved is an exhilarating and strengthening sensation.

CaringBridge entry for February 12, 2009

I'm done! :::hands in the air, doin a jig:::

While I'm elated that I'm done being tied to a table by my face then blasted with photons, the effects of radiation are cumulative. Which means, as this is the peak of my treatments, it's also the peak of the pain. However, the hydrocodone works pretty well, and I guess adrenaline has kicked in a bit because I don't feel all that bad right now.

Radiation Doc says my throat looks horrible just like it should, and I should start feeling some improvements over the next couple of weeks. I go back to see him in a month for follow up. I'll see my ENT in a month as well, then every month for the first year. Every other month for the second year, every third month for the third year . . . you get the picture. We follow that patter for five years. After that I'll just need an annual check, and at 10 years I'm officially "cured." I put that in quotes because there's nothing certain about any of this. Just percentages. Thankfully mine look very good.

The staff there gave me a nice graduation certificate and took pictures. Lisa did bunny ears over my head while I was tied down . . . so not fair. And, yes, we all skipped down the hall one last time.

I'll keep updating this site after each appointment and if anything noteworthy happens in between. Like puking maybe. Well . . . y'all have had enough of that, I'm sure, so maybe not.

Thanks for being there for me, all of you. I can't begin to tell you how your presence in my life has helped me do the little things. Like sit up in bed at 6:35 in the morning, get up and get going for work. Eat even though my mouth was on fire and my throat ached. My strength and drive came from knowing you were there.

I have to say that I did imagine y'all's voices like the guy from the movie *Waterboy*. "You can do eeet!" Always made me smile.

Much love,

Ed

responses

YAHOO!!! I'm so glad you are all done -- you are such a ray of bright light --
I just know that over the next few weeks you will begin to feel better and better, and one day you will have a great story to share with all your great-great-grandchildren!
Sending super huge hugs today -- so duck!
Jo Dee

Amazing...that's what you are! Congrats on making it thru the treatments. You and Debbie continue to be a source of strength and an example of hope and faith.
Bet you didn't realize how much you'd be giving others thru this journey, huh?!?
Much love from the frozen north of Vermont.
Kelli

A poem in honor of your last treatment (A Haiku)
**Radiation sucks
Thank freakin God its over
Let healing begin!**
Love, us
Amy

Congrats!!! You are amazing --
we hope to come to the beach this summer and see you skip in person.
Myrna

YEAH!!! I am glad for you that this stage is over.
On to healing up completely and being cancer free!!
Grizelle

Why do I always cry at radiation graduations?...
Congratulations!!
Bert

Ed, great going. Judy and I will continue to include you in our prayers.
By the way, I golf with a guy who had similar throat cancer and he is doing great! Like you said, he visits his doctor once a month, and so far he is cancer free. We think of you both often and will see you in May if not sooner.
Butch

responses

Huzzah/hooray for the end of photons! You've been a real inspiration, Ed.

My clan will all be continuing our prayers for your full recovery.

Meantime, I believe I will skip to work tomorrow in tribute to you and your amazing spirit.

Love,
Blake

We continue to have you in our prayers as you deal with the continued effects of the treatments! You're a true inspiration!!!! Love ya!!!

Ginny

So, so, so happy for you that you're through with the treatments and on the way to being pain free!

We are so happy for you that the treatments have ended and will continue to think of you through the weeks and months ahead. YOU are such an inspiration, Ed!

I always smile and giggle after reading your journal entries ~ you have such a great attitude... even when life gives you a curve ball!!!

We love you and Debbie and miss you at HRBC, but we're connected by spirit ~ that is a great feeling, right? Hope today is a good one!

Love, Janet and Wayne

HOORAY!!!!!!!!!!!!

We're all so proud of the graceful and poignant way you have shared your journey with us --

HALLELUJAH!!!!!

each phase clearly CHALLENGING, and you did sooooooooo very well! I understand that you'll be dealing with this and the side effects for quite a bit longer, so you need to know that we're going to continue to be in our prayers! Take good care and give wonderful Debbie all our love as well!

Katherine and Dan

Most excellent, Ed...I mean the fact that you're done. I don't want you to get the big head or something, like you're most excellent

or...even if you are...to which I'm not certain about, although...nevermind, just getting deeper. We're here cause we care, and we thank you for carrying us during this time and letting us be a part of your journey. Love to you both!!

Danny

Dear Ed,

The path you took during this whole experience has been an inspiration to all who know you.

Best wishes for the road ahead.

Keep skipping, what a great image.

Even though we haven't written after each blog, we have read them and have prayed for you each time.

Janet and Harold

CaringBridge entry for February 16, 2009

Radiation Doc clarified something for me today. When I heard him say that I should feel some improvement over the next couple of weeks, I missed the part where he said I'll probably feel worse first. Which explains this morning and why I called him.

I would have sworn I had swallowed a whole bundle of barbed wire when I first woke up. So I downed a bunch of my hydrocodone, called my guys to let them know there wouldn't be work today and then passed out until just before noon. That's when I called Doc.

"I need more drugs."

"I told you things might get worse and you might want a pain patch."

"I wasn't listening. Only heard the good parts."

So I'm going by tomorrow morning and picking up more prescriptions from him to manage things over the next few days.

On the weight front, this eating oatmeal and soup three times a day just isn't cutting it, and Debbie says I'm looking very skinny. I weigh just over 140 pounds. Since I can stomach the protein drinks again, I'll begin drinking them twice a day to supplement my soup diet. That should help. Meanwhile, the phone keeps ringing with work (thank God), so I'm trying to move things fast enough to get it all done and keep the customers happy (help me, God).

Hey Ed...wow, all that oatmeal! They say that it can greatly reduce cholesterol...
your cholesterol level must be perfect...
or better even! I hope an attempt at humor (okay, a small attempt) at least got a smile. We're hanging in there with ya...is my room ready??? Looking forward to your next update.

Danny

Ed, it is time to slow down and heal, brother.

Can you take some time off and watch movies while having some good couch time?! (I know "couch time" usually means time in someone's office, but in this case it means time on your sofa!)

Sending you peace and healing.

Love, Betty & Mike

Dear Ed,

I'm glad you are going for the patch, and I certainly hope that it will provide a good deal of comfort! I'm sure that your clients understand and are in your corner. Take good care of yourself right now! In our prayers,

Dan and Katherine

So glad to hear you had your last treatment last week. You have had a tough road to travel the last several months, but your determination, your great sense of humor and the inspiration from all your friends got you through the rough times. **Things will get better in time.** You have both been in our thoughts and prayers and will continue to be.

Love, Karen and Ray

Sendin all the good vibes I can, brother...
keep ya head up! Chris

Ed -- I've been reading your journal often. **You've been through a lot since I saw you over the holidays.** It's great to know that your treatments are done, and you can start the process of getting back to some normalcy. You have been in our prayers, and we hope the worst is over. I look forward to catching up with you again the next time you are in Richmond. Best, John and Doreene

---

Well, darn it all. It's good you were focusing on the good news from your doc, bad that you woke up with all that barbed wire. By this time, we trust you have the patch and are feeling better.
Wow! The important thing is you have finished your treatments and will go up from here to better health and better feeling each day. Our prayers continue with all your other good friends and family. We love both of you and look forward to when we can visit again!

Love, Bob and Esther

We have been following your progress and have been very impressed by your optimism and determination.
Hang in there. You are amazing! We send good wishes and prayers your way. Hello to Debbie!

Nancy and Mitch

CaringBridge entry for February 17, 2009

Aahaallllll righty then. I've got my patch on and just popped a Percocet. Time to lie on the couch and read until I can't focus. Shouldn't take too long.

I didn't have much trouble diverting my mind from the pain today. Had a very busy morning that lasted until about 1 p.m. getting the guys going on their stuff, picking up a counter top and a couple of trees, meeting with an electrician at a house for some work that had to be done today (they're closing on Friday), fixing a friend's door that wasn't shutting correctly. Then in the afternoon I installed the countertop, did some tiling and sheetrock mudding in the "coaching" mode and picked up my meds at about 4:30 from the pharmacy.

When I picked up my prescriptions, I asked where I'm supposed to put this patch thingy.

"On my shoulder or something?"

"Just ask your pharmacist where you should stick it."

"Not this pharmacist. He's a good friend and a Carolina fan."

Debbie said, "In that case, just tell him he has to apply it."

After a brief discussion he said to just put it on my torso someplace.

Done.

responses

Hi Ed,

Don't know how you keep going, but I'm glad you do.

If you get toooo skinny, find a way for a transfer and I will gladly give you 20, 30 or 40 pounds.

Keep the good attitude you have.

Love, Sandra

I don't know how you do it, but just keep on doin' it.

Sounds like today was better than yesterday.

Here's to more and more better days for you!

Love, Blake

OK, now, sounds like a much better day and some sweet dreams coming your way!?!

One can't be too careful w/ those Carolina fans if you are a self-proclaimed DUKE Man...good cautionary question on your part!

Take good care, eat, sleep...eat, eat, eat!

Love to you and Debbie both,

Dan and Katherine

CaringBridge entry for February 24, 2009

Well, it's been a week since my last update and 12 days since my final radiation treatment, but who's counting. Actually, I had to look up the date and do subtraction to figure out how many days it has been. It was that or take off one shoe and sock so I could count all the way backward.

The pain patches are doing the trick. I only have to use the lidocaine rinse stuff at night when I wake up. My throat gets pretty dry at night and one swallow still can wake me up. But I'm not taking any of the other stuff that's been prescribed because I haven't needed it. My throat also feels pretty tight, and I still feel a twinge when I first open my mouth to eat. So I'm trying to stretch my mouth during the day by opening up wide to see if I can get some elasticity back. I don't think I could floss if I wanted to yet. But I don't want to because touching my teeth near my gums still gives me the willies. Brushing is a very gentle process I can assure you.

My energy level is definitely picking back up. Getting that hitch back into my giddy up so to speak. However, everything else is pretty much the same. No hair around my head and face, very little saliva and the same nasty taste problems. My teeth aren't as sore, so I'm moving back to Chunky soup, which is a plus because there are more calories in 'em. But it's still chicken noodle something and seafood something. Amy found some excellent lobster bisque at Costco that has like 380 calories a serving, and I eat at least two servings in every bowl. I'll be killing that off tomorrow at lunch.

I did try a corn chip yesterday because I saw the bag in the pantry and am just dying to taste real food again. Took a bite, even swallowed it. Along with half a glass of water. It was a little like super absorbent cardboard.

I want my taste buds back!

responses

You're not taking any of the other stuff that's been prescribed?

A corn chip?

:)

Scott

You're a soldier, man... real inspirational...

thanks for keeping us in the loop, Ed.

Love you so much!

Chris

Hi Ed and Debbie,

Glad the patch is helping. Lobster Bisque, what a great idea. I still have the memory of you guys introducing me to "all the crab legs you can eat" at restaurant in Savannah. Your treat.

Let's make plans to do that again as soon as the throat allows. Our treat!

I'm sure Ed and Lynda will want to come along. Thank you both for many good times. We're expecting the best and have already thanked God for His good work in you.

Love, Janet

Thanks for another candid update. We are constantly amazed at how you keep all of us informed and...entertained! We are glad to hear that each day seems to find you gaining strength and dropping some symptoms of your radiation. Lobster bisque sounds good (yeah, Amy!), and chunky over smooth soup is great to hear. We keep praying for you and Debbie and hope your enjoyment of more food will increase each day.

We hope the barbed wire in your throat is becoming a thing of the past and are grateful that, hopefully, it disappears after swallowing like smoke (yes, that's a weak attempt at humor!).

We love you and trust that the prayers of all of us keep warming the cockles of your heart!

Love, Bob and Esther

CaringBridge entry for February 27, 2009

Yesterday I noticed I was gagging a little again, and I choked several times drinking water. Kept going down the wrong pipe. I just kept feeling like I needed to clear my throat. So last night I got the mini flashlight out and tried to look at my throat. Because of all the swelling I haven't been able to see anything past my tongue in some time. Same was true last night. So I used my finger to press down on my tongue and get it out of the way. Low and behold, my throat looks a lot like it did after the tonsillectomy. Much of what should be pink was sort of white and a little goopy everywhere.

Good news/not such good news for me. Good news: That white stuff is the mucous membrane healing up. Not such good news: I'm sloughing off the bad layers and scabs (do you ever really get "scabs" in your mouth and throat?) and either coughing them up or swallowing them. Hence the choking and little sharp pains back there. Especially in the morning. Kinda gross, I know.

Still, that means I'm moving along. I don't have any sores around my tongue anymore. I like that.

Actually tried to floss, VERY gently, last night. Felt like the floss was cold. Man, my gums are in lousy shape right now. I've been rinsing with that Biotene stuff, which is supposed to help fight bacteria, etc. I haven't gotten any infections so far, so I guess it's working.

Five of my bottom teeth are looking a little iffy still, but none are loose. Here's to hoping they make it. I'm not thrilled at the prospect of going through more oral surgery at the moment.

Off to work. Finishing up a big job today and want to make the house pretty for when the owners come down and see it.

responses

Ed, Durham just hosted a horror film festival. I think you should have been here to show your stuff.

You're amazing to continue to see the light at the end of the tunnel...or down the throat, as it were. There's a Lenten prayer that might be apt for you, both for the Season and for your chemo wilderness journey. It's by Peter Mead. Lord, sanctify the silence with which we contemplate your boundless love for sinners, your sacrifice so great. And grant us hope and patience that, when the fast is gone, new songs of "Alleluia" may greet your Easter dawn!

Lori

---

eeeeeeeeeewwwwwwwww grosssssss!

I want some throat pics!

Chris

Glad to hear that you're making good progress (although I guess it doesn't feel very good).

Thanks for the updates, I always pass them on to Mom, Dad and Val. Here's to healing.

Blake

Hi, Ed and Debbie! Still praying for you all.

I've learned to read Ed's updates on an empty stomach...ha ha.

At least the gross stuff these days seems to be a getting better gross stuff.

Bert

Wow -- yuck doesn't quite fit the magnitude of what you are experiencing. Your selflessness in sharing such a difficult personal time with your family and friends with such humor and grace goes to the person you are inside and out. Its a true lesson to everyone how precious our time here on Earth -- and you are an example of how we should all live our lives.

In short, you are my hero!

And you happen to be married to another of my personal heros, so extra points for that! Eat some organic nonfat yogurt -- lots of good bacteria to counter all the bad stuff. I know it sounds good, huh?

<:) Jo Dee

Hey there, bro! Just wanted to say that we love you! I was thinking about the stories of "that weird/cool patient" the nurses and docs are going to be talking about for years to come...

you might even become an urban legend of sorts...

the patient who skipped, even radiation couldn't stop the jokes!!!!!

Hugs again, though none are big enough.

Donya

Whoa, that blows! !!!!!!! Choking on scabs may be necessary, but geeeeez. :(You're healing though, so yay for that. :) and of course happy about the work.

Can't wait for you to taste that flan I had --

make her make you another one when your able to. It was really good.

Kiss Debbie for me. :)

Scott

Wow! Your visuals are...well, visual!

Still praying... In His Love, Janne

CaringBridge entry for February 27, 2009

When Debbie came back from her latest business trip I told her, "This is the first time I've felt like a cancer patient."

It was a very rough week.

The thing I had somehow managed to avoid, getting sick, finally happened.

Sunday morning Debbie and I were doing our usual pre-everything-that-happens-in-the-morning, Then I said, "I'm going to take a shower so I can make it to Sunday School!" I got about things. Come to think of it, that's our routine pre-everything-that-happens-in-the-morning. Then I said, "I'm going to take a shower so I can make it to Sunday School!" I got to the bathroom, started to get undressed then had the sudden urge to vomit. And I did, but just a little. Debbie called down the hall when she heard me spit into the toilet, "What was that?"

"Nothing, just gagged a little." Then I really threw up.

"That didn't sound like nothing."

We figured I had The Plague, so I rinsed my mouth out and went back to bed. Very tired.

I felt a little better in the afternoon, and Monday I went off to work as usual. I felt very rundown but wanted to keep moving, and I figured I would just push through this like usual. That worked until mid-morning when I went back out to my truck to get some channel-locks (pliers) to work on a sink I was replacing and threw up. And didn't stop throwing up for several minutes. Afterward, I didn't feel all that bad, just woozy, but I knew I would be able to get through the rest of the day.

"Tomorrow I'll get some antibiotics for this stuffed up nose," I thought.

I got the guys going Tuesday morning then ran up to Home Depot, then to a Realtor's office to pick up a key and made a call to my Now Family Doctor to get in for some drugs to help me out. No dice. Booked through the month, one doctor down, flu's going around. "Nice, now what?" I thought, and the receptionist then suggested I hit the Urgent Care facility. She pulled up my file while we were talking and knew enough to tell me to hurry and get some medication because getting sick right now is bad. She didn't tell me all that, she just told me to go to Urgent Care and I shouldn't wait.

It makes a big difference when people do their jobs well. Thank you, receptionist!

journal

At Urgent Care I was told that while my white blood counts were very low, there was no doubt I had a sinus infection. Since I had just been through radiation treatments, my immune system was worthless, so they went with some big gun antibiotic that even my Carolina Fan Pharmacist said, "Man! They're not fooling around!" But the sinus infection was just the beginning.

That night I realized I did have The Plague after all. And no way to fight it.

Viruses suck.

Leaving out the gory details, I'll just say that while I am finally able to think clearly enough to type this, I'm now down to 125 pounds and have never felt so helpless in my life. But I am vertical at the moment, and I have an incredible wife and family and marvelously supportive friends. The hair on my face is coming back here and there, my throat doesn't really hurt much and my taste buds made some progress as well. Not to mention that breakfast AND lunch have stayed in me today.

So far so good.

PS: Pray for "Skip." He's a guy I met last week who I was supposed to do some work for today. He went up to Chesapeake for another two- or three-day round of chemo but has wound up being hospitalized. He's going to be there the next three to four weeks. Says we'll install his dryer vent when he gets home.

ED...IT WAS **MALIGNANT.**

responses

I am sorry you are having to go through this.

My prayers are with you.

Myrna

Hope you hang on to dinner as well. Made a spur of the moment trip to Duck to work on sister-in-law Katie's house. We will be coming back in 2-3 weeks.

Once I get a firm date maybe we could work out a glass of water somewhere.

Was going to say a Capt. Franks dog but probably not a good idea yet.

Our thoughts are with you.

Miles

Ed and Debbie,

Well that really bites! But, we're glad that you are (once again) on the mend, Ed.

Perhaps a little more REST before you go full tilt?

Heck, we get tired just reading about all that you both do on a regular basis!!

We will keep you and your friend Skip in our prayers.

Love, Sue and John

Ed — I love you so much,

I wish I could be there and actually be helpful!

We were both down for 3 weeks — this flu is just lousy. Please please be careful until your immune system gets back to normal!!!! I am so grateful that God let me have you as a brother.

Please rest and take it easy!

Hugs, Donya

Dear Ed, I continue to pray for your recovery.

Glad the plague hasn't affected your sense of humor and your ability to write most of the gory details.

I enjoy your regular updates. Take care.

Joyce

Hi Ed, I'm glad you're feeling better. Harry H told me you were under the weather.

Just what you didn't need.

It's good to read your updates to know what's going on. Hang in there, kid, cause we all love ya and want you back out with us again having fun. Take care and say hi to Debbie for me.

Luv, Barb

responses

Hang in there, Ed. It must be hard just to get the words typed out when you're feeling so sick.

But looking ahead, just think of how much fun you'll have putting the weight back on!

Love, Blake

You are totally amazing. I'd probably go to bed for a week.

You set an excellent example for weaklings like me.

Keep mending, keep eating and keep it down!

Anne

Amazing and downright saint-like!...

with all that's going on you close with an ask for prayers for others...

you're incredible.

Dwayne

123? That's a good wrestling weight!

Think of how small those guys are! You'll kick ass!

Chris

Text Message, March 6, 2008

My step-daughter Ashley had these words of encouragement for me:

"If u r trying to compete with me for skinniest bitch, u only have a few pounds to go! I am the skinny bitch in this family. Eat something! And stop puking it up!"

Obviously, she wasn't going to let that title slip away easily, so I might as well try to eat.

When they told me my immune system would be weakened by radiation,

I never thought much of it.

My immune system has always been pretty strong, so I figured I just stood a slightly larger chance of catching a cold or something. I respected all the instructions regarding brushing my teeth gently with a new soft bristle tooth brush, but I never thought I was trying to avoid even the slightest infection. The point they were making was stiffer bristles would rub my gums raw, exposing them to harmful bacteria. "Harmful" being a far more meaningful word than the way I was used to understanding it.

So when I woke up that Monday morning with a stuffed up nose and proceeded to blow large quantities of thick, green snot out, I knew that I had a sinus infection. However, my first reaction imitated any previous time I had come across a tissue like the one I saw that morning: I took a Sudafed and went on to work. Dry it up, kill the bacteria and get on with my week. I've done it a million times.

Not this time.

When I woke up Tuesday my nose was worse and had been all night. Therefore, I didn't breathe through my nose, I breathed through my mouth. Major mistake since my throat was trying to heal up. Now when I began to drink, all that white stuff lining my throat that used to be healing membrane was now very dry and bleeding around the edges. Not to mention a whole lot more painful to live with.

I swished with some magic mouthwash and went off to work, promising to call Family Doctor to get some antibiotics.

As you saw in my journal entry, Family Doc was booked up, but the receptionist had the foresight to send me over to the Urgent Care facility on the beach. I had to go up the beach anyway, so I made that one of my stops.

Now, an Urgent Care facility during flu season really becomes a Not So Urgent Care facility. I was there three hours before I saw the Physician's Assistant. She was terrific, though, and very thorough. After going over my symptoms and background, she went through all the regular questions I've answered a hundred times in life.

"Are you allergic to anything?"

"Nope."

"Are you currently taking any medications?"

"Nope. (two beats) Wait! Of course I am geez!"

Old habits keep rearing up.

I proceeded to go over the various medicines I was taking for thrush, pain, etc. Of course I didn't bring a single one with me, so we had to kind of play Guess the Anti-Fungal Med until I knew we had them all just right.

She decided to take a blood sample and do some basic blood-work so she could see where things were with me. I wondered why I hadn't had any blood-work done during my treatments, but I guess that's because they know what they're going to see. Zilch. No white blood cells, no lymph gland activity, no cholesterol, etc, etc, etc. No lymph blood did tell me I didn't have to worry about high cholesterol or becoming diabetic due to massive weight gain while undergoing treatment.

She came back with a print-out and showed me what should have been a heads up for that night.

"It's obvious from your symptoms that you have a sinus infection. Now, a normal person's white blood cell count should be between these numbers," she pointed to a 4.5 and a 10.5 on the page.

She went on, "When you have an infection your number here should be high. Yours is a 5."

"That's not high." I am so observant.

"No, but that's due to the radiation. That 5 is higher than it was before the infection is my guess."

"So mine was probably not even on that scale to begin with."

"That's right," she continued. "Now, when your body is dealing with a virus this next line gets elevated."

She pointed to an abbreviation of LY and when she mentioned it had something to do with my lymph system I knew I was in trouble here.

"Normal on this line should be between 20.5 and 51.1."

Mine was an 11.8.

"So I'm probably not dealing with a virus right now, right?" I said not very convincingly.

"Ummm, no I think you might have one going, too."

"Not much you can prescribe for that, huh." Captain Obvious strikes again.

She filled out the prescription for some horse pill-sized antibiotics and told me to drink lots of liquids and get some rest. I went on my way, worked the rest of the day and after a meeting at church that night I finally followed that last instruction.

The flu kicked in that night and later I would realize that the 11.8 I had meant there was nothing my body had to fight that virus. Weakened immune system? You betcha.

I proceeded to be more violently ill than I had been in my whole life and I had hepatitis once. With nothing but soup as a staple it didn't take even the first vomiting session to empty my stomach, but I wasn't done then. Oh no. I would dry heave for the next six or eight hours. I

kept thinking that this was more like having a seizure than throwing up.

Then the diarrhea started up. Or down as the case may be.

Once again, since everything in me was pretty much liquid you would think that would have been over in a heartbeat, but it wasn't.

I would wind up panting on the bathroom floor, my throat burning from being dry, so I'd drink water. It was like there was a straight tube from my mouth to my anus, only for whatever reason the tube had to be painfully squeezed halfway down before letting loose out the other side.

It was not quite morning and I knew I could get into some serious trouble with dehydration, so I unplugged my cell phone and turned it on and kept it with me. I decided on a couple of tests for myself and committed to calling 911 if either occurred. First was if I messed the bed. If I couldn't wake up in time, or wasn't capable of getting myself down the hall, it was time to go to the hospital. The second was if I saw something completely out of line. Like if Debbie was suddenly home. I knew she was traveling on business and that I would love to have her here right now to watch out for me. So if she were suddenly at the bedside, I would be hallucinating and it is time to go to the hospital.

In hindsight, if I was thinking that much about it I should have just called 911 and said, "Come get me."

But I made it through the night, called one customer in the morning

ED...IT WAS **MALIGNANT.**

saying I couldn't get to her right then and would call back and called my guys.

"I'm sorry, but I can't do it," I told one of them. "Flu."

He told me to just take care, but I knew it was going to hurt all of them not to be able to work for the next couple of days. I hated that so much. They depend on me for their income right now, and I was going to have to cut them out of three days' pay.

Later that day I spoke to Debbie on the phone and she offered to come home immediately. I told her "no" because there truly wasn't anything she could do for me and I was just going to sleep until it was all over. I told her about work and the guys and she told me to not to worry about it and stay in bed until she got back on Friday. Just rest. Advice I couldn't physically refuse at the moment.

I was able to get to the shower that evening and got cleaned up. I felt like I was dragging a couple of hundred extra pounds with me as I moved like a zombie. I put on new underwear and jeans and stood in front of the mirror to start brushing my teeth. Just then I felt this warm trickle running down the back of my right thigh. I was crapping on myself and hadn't even farted.

Just lovely.

I stepped right back into the shower, jeans and all, got undressed and cleaned up again. Afterward I had to walk down my hall naked and shivering like I was outside during a Siberian winter, get new clothes

and bundle back up. This time I kept myself together and passed back out in bed. The whole affair had worn me out.

I pretty much slipped in and out of consciousness for the next day, then I got up and weighed myself on Friday morning.

On Tuesday at Urgent Care I had weighed 141 pounds. Friday morning I weighed 121. I had lost 20 pounds in less than three days. Didn't think that was possible.

"That can't be healthy," I said out loud.

My vision stayed very blurred so I called Carolina Fan Pharmacist Friend and he said, "Rehydrate, rehydrate, rehydrate. Dehydration can cause double vision."

I drank some water and worried that it would start shooting out of me again, but it didn't. I forced myself out to the store and bought some Gatorade and started chugging. Very slowly I began to feel more normal but incredibly weak.

As Debbie drove up I stood in the hallway and cried. I couldn't help the relief I felt at having her there with me again.

I figured I had just gotten a glimpse of what other cancer patients and chronically ill people have to deal with on a longer term or even permanent basis. I felt a little guilty because I'm done with my treatments and by all accounts it's over for me. I mean, sure, right now my butt cheeks don't touch together, leaving an unfamiliar and uncomfortable void, but I'll get that back. Then I won't have to worry about any whistling noises if I'm standing outside on a windy day.

I knew all this was just a small setback that was pretty much in the rear view mirror and I'd be back to normal in no time.

"I have got it so easy."

CaringBridge entry for March 9, 2009

For the first time in this process I'm actually going to voluntarily take some time off. The fact that I get winded walking up one flight of stairs is pretty much the reason for it. Not to mention the reality that if I got the flu again (there's nothing in me to stop it), it would probably kill me. Folks were ticked that I didn't go to the hospital as it is to keep fluids in me.

So I'm being extra careful. Staying away from crowded places, not shaking hands, carrying hand sanitizer (and even using it some) and drinking/taking supplements like crazy. My weight bottomed out at 121 on Friday morning. Losing 20 pounds in less than 3 days is sort of hard on the body, and I'm still pretty beat. I haven't weighed that much since my junior year in high school during wrestling season, and I was almost 4 inches shorter than I am now. Ridiculous.

Good news is I've all ready got 5 or 6 pounds back, there's no more double vision from the dehydration and my customers love me because they're all cool with waiting a few days to let me catch my breath.

Thank you all for the postings and the calls the last couple of days. I didn't mean to scare anyone with the last posting, but it was a pretty scary, and tough, experience. But it's also over, and as long as I'm alive when something's happened, I'll hop on here and tell y'all about it.

Love ya much!!

responses

Hi there! I must admit, I did wonder what to say -- and Jeff wants you to know that anyone that can keep me quiet for any period of time is a saint under any conditions... ~ <:)

I think about you every day and want you to know that you will be ok. What a trial you are all going through. It's an honor to be a part of this with you all, and if there were anything we could do to take some of the pain and hardship away, we would at the drop of a hat!

Get some rest -- and yes, get to the hospital -- no one can get fluids into you faster than they can, and you need to stay hydrated! Drink those Emergen Cs all day long, they are loaded with potassium, which is what you need too....

We are sending you so much love and hugs and smooches to keep you going -- rent Galaxy Quest -- seriously the funniest thing I have seen ever...which actually explains a lot about me... hummmmmmm

and don't forget You Tube for funny animal videos.

Jeff starts his Broadway show tomorrow. It's called *It Ain't Nothing But the Blues*, and he woke up last night from a dream where he forgot his guitar on opening night. So I'll be bringing an extra one with me just in case <:)

Super big hugs and you take care -- extra hug to Debbie...

Jo Dee

Being at a loss for something profound to say, I'll just say what I'm thinking.

Cancer sucks and needs to be beaten every chance that comes up.

From what I keep seeing from your notes, you are doing it. I know it isn't easy. Keep it up, but get some rest once in a while!! My thoughts are with you.

Ed

I love you so much.

Difficult for me to read, but thank you for keeping it all out there in the open for those who love you.

I hope you can feel the love and strength from all of us.

Mom

Yeah, word on the street is that things get worse after the treatments before they start to get better. You seem to be a shining example of that.

So chill and let your body heal.

We're praying...

Bert

Ed and Debbie, just a note to let you know we're still here....reading and praying for your recovery. You know one thing I learned a long time ago is...you're known by the company you keep...and in reading the remarks from folks who love you guys, y'all keep good company!

I'm sure you already know or have heard this before, but it's not faith until you have to trust it.

Love you guys,
Danny and Susan

CaringBridge entry for March 12, 2009

I just got back from the first of 12 post-treatment exams with my ENT. He looked over the notes and at my weight, looked at me and said, "Twenty pounds??"

"Uh. Yeah."

"How do you lose twenty pounds? Water mostly?"

"I didn't see any organs," I replied, "and everything seems to be working okay, so I think I've still got most of the important stuff."

He just shook his head.

He numbed my sinus cavities and ran that flexible scope thing into my head through my nose and back down my throat. Had me sing "eeeeeeeee" a couple of times then checked the other nostril.

"Things look great," he said. "No sign of lesions or growths, and everything is healing up very well. Also there's no sign of any smoldering areas. Your sinuses look pretty clear."

"Sweet."

We talked about my complete lack of white blood cells at the moment and anything else in me that would help fight an illness and what I need to do to steer clear of getting sick.

"Nothing is here to stop you from getting the very same flu, or any other illness, immediately," he informed me. "But you're a month out of radiation and your body should be rebuilding right now and getting stronger every day. You just have to help it out for a while."

So we added a couple of things to my already disgusting getting ready for bed ritual.

I have these canisters of saline under pressure that I spray up my nose and inhale until I can pretty much drink the liquid through my nose. That makes sure my sinuses are completely clear of any blockages and helps rinse out any viruses that might have set up in there. But that much saline has a very drying effect, and in the morning I wake up with a bloody nose. So I've got some steroid spray I spritz up my nose in the morning and some gel that I smear in the front of my nose to try and keep things moist. I'm supposed to do the saline and gel several times a day.

journal

You should see and hear that affair. I can't quite snort all the liquid up my nose, so part way through this stuff tends to pour down my face. I lean way over the sink and just let it run off then wash my face when I'm done.

So attractive. I make sure Debbie's not even within earshot when I go through this routine.

In all my clothes, including shoes, and after drinking about a gallon of water, I weighed 135. I've been getting about 3,000 calories a day in the last three days, including a plate of spaghetti last night. I should be able to get some serious carbs in me now that I can chew and eat that!

My taste buds seem to improve daily, and I can make saliva if I try, which is a nice sign this early on. My energy level is coming back up as well, so I'll continue to eat bunches and lay around throughout the weekend to keep myself moving in the right direction.

If I can avoid getting sick again, I should have pretty smooth sailing ahead.

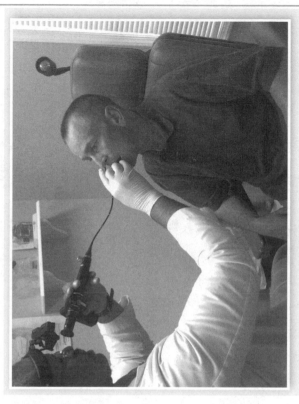

The Scope

You are a true hero the way you have been handling this, Ed.

I feel like such a loser complaining about anything in my life. Keep eating and getting back to your best weight -- we are all thinking about you constantly and sending positive thoughts and virtual hugs! Hugs and a shout out to all your family too....

Jo Dee

Ed,
You are truly amazing! Keep up the good work and enjoy the 3,000 calories a day....

I know you are younger than us to be able to eat like that!!!

Love, Betty & Mike

Ok, Ed. By the time this is over -- and it will be --

you will be such an expert in the medical field that you will be able to add an MD consulting to your CALLED.

What can we contribute to your 3,000 calories a day---just name it and we will prepare it and drive down to deliver it.

Ed

Well, that was a little too much information for me (your squeamish friend), but at least no blood was involved! I have never passed out at the computer and don't want to start now.

I am SO glad that you can now have REAL food.

God indeed is good, all the time!! We'll be in Richmond for a long weekend, but as soon as we get back, I'll call you and see what kind of goodies we can cook up for you.

Much love and continuing prayers,

Sandy and Jeff

Roll on, Ed. Sounds great!

Miles

Ed, your good news was announced last night at our Lenten "soup and bread" dinner!

Everyone applauded and wishes you continued health and well-being. These are the folks who have been praying, too. I can't thank you enough for calling me yesterday!

Lots of love, Mom

Ed, It is great to hear you are continuing to make progress.

The night-time ritual sounds like a real winner.

The therapy from my back surgery was a walk in the park compared to what you are going through. That reminds me, I have to do my sit-ups. I am thrilled you are doing so well!!

David

One month out of radiation, one week past the Plague,

and the healing picked up speed.

Thank you, God!

The strides my taste buds made over those couple of days were incredible. Everything I tried seemed to taste just about normal again already. With things having been so nasty for so long I was still wading back into the food pool very slowly, but loving every minute of it.

When Debbie and I tried a fancy coffee-type drink awhile back, I noticed that vanilla was a sweetener and flavor that worked for me. The coffee flavor seemed to help too, so I used that as the basis for some experimentation. I would brew a pot of decaf coffee then scoop chocolate ice cream into a mug then add the coffee on top. That made the whole drink lukewarm and it tasted okay as well. I knew I was getting some good calories this way so I just kept doing it. Low and behold the chocolate began to taste like chocolate. I also began to taste the sweetness of the sugar as well. So I began to mix the coffee with ice

ED...IT WAS **MALIGNANT**.

cream and top it with whipped cream. Awesome!

Along with the sweet buds working again, other food started tasting good as well. Just a couple of days after that I began eating spaghetti, so I decided to try and expand my range again. With the limited supply of saliva I had, it was necessary to keep to "wet" foods, so my next foray was into Shepherd's Pie, broccoli and cheese and spiced apples. Another success! Everything tasted SO good. I still had to drink three glasses of water with lunch, but I knew I'd be gaining my weight and energy back quickly now that I could eat again.

The whole thing really boosted my mood.

As I was up checking email I had my iPod on shuffle and on came Earth, Wind and Fire with "Serpentine Fire." I stood up, started shuffling with the intro beats across the floor toward the door to get some more water and when that first blast of horns hit in the song I threw up my hands, tossed my head back and yelled along, "Yeeeeaaaahhhhhh!" Then danced all over the upstairs. Doing some line dance disco steps from high school, spinning around . . . the whole Saturday Night Fever deal.

That song was followed up by the Commodores doing "Too Hot to Trot."

By then I noticed how winded I was, so I toned down the dancing a bit but couldn't wipe the smile off my face for anything.

Caring Bridge entry for March 14, 2009

I uploaded a couple of new pictures so you could get a peek at this ridiculously skinny body I've got going at the moment. I am back to about 130, and my energy is climbing back to normal. 155 seems so far away at the moment.

Once again I wanted to thank all of you for the guestbook entries. Your words of encouragement have quite literally fed me during this time. Very often I would come on this site to go back and reread certain entries so I could reconnect with that feeling I got the first time I saw it. When I was struggling, I could get an immediate fix that lifted my spirits, challenged me to keep on and helped me to keep my sense of humor and perspective on all this. I got all of that from your words. From your effort to communicate and support me. From your friendship.

Thank you all.

Now some encouragement from me: You guys did some incredible stuff here with me, so don't stop with me. I'm certainly not the only person you've heard of with a serious illness. So I'm not the only person you can lift out of a rough patch. I want you to be aware of the power you have at your fingertips and the impact you can have on the lives of other people and inspire you to offer that to others as often as an opportunity comes around. Trust me on this: You can't possibly overestimate the positive effect a sincerely kind word can have on someone in need.

God bless all of you.

PS. If you're able, kick some cash toward CaringBridge. The tool they have created here performs an incredible service for people facing some desperate times. And while there is no cost to any of us to take advantage of it, it's not like it doesn't cost a thing to be out here and available. Thanks.

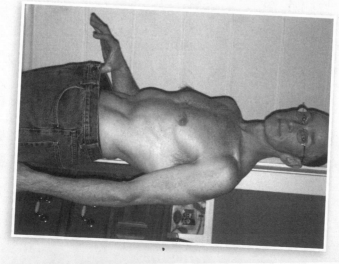

Me at about 130 lbs. in my 32-inch waist jeans fresh out of the dryer. Ewwwww.

responses

Ed, so glad you're gaining some weight and feeling a little better. Your spirits have been so good through all of this, you are an inspiration. You're a sweetheart and we all love you.

Hang in there and soon you'll be back to your "normal crazy" self.

Love ya,
Barb

YIKES
your body is literally hanging from your cheek bones -- stop it!
I'm thinking sticks of butter?
Maybe we start the morning with bacon fat. !!
Scott

There once was a lymph named node
Who was supposed to make a shitload
Of white blood cells for Ed
But poor lymph node was dead
Glad to hear you are back on Well Road

Amy

We have been out of town much of the time since the first of the year, and it has been a wonderful thing to be able to keep in touch with your progress no matter where we were. We have been inspired by your sense of humor even in the darkest of days. You would have loved my Grandmother Grace whose motto was, "You might as well laugh as cry". She was one special lady, and your tenacity ranks right up there with hers! (That's about the highest compliment there is!) Debbie, we marvel at your strength and dedication as you share in this unexpected adventure. What a blessing you are to each other during this detour.

God has given you the amazing ability to minister to others even as He and others continue to minister to you.

Your frank and honest acceptance of the cards you have been dealt has inspired others to look beyond the moment and focus toward better things yet to come. What a gift to receive and to share!! We are proud to know you and call you our friends.

May God's healing hand continue to be upon you as you trust Him to guide you through all the days ahead. May you continue to find sunshine and laughter even in the dark moments. May you always be willing to share yourself so openly and honestly with others.

We are not alone, God is Good, All the Time!
God Bless you, both of you!!!
Susan and Joe

CaringBridge entry for April 1, 2009

Well, yesterday I had my final visit with Radiation Doc, and everything looks great. He examined my neck and clavicle region, looked into my mouth and checked out my gums, tongue and throat, then said, "Sorry about this next part, but it's easier to feel bumps then see them and I need to check out the original sight." He proceeded to put on a latex glove and sanitize it with that alcohol wash stuff, then he reached down my throat and started pushing around where my left tonsil used to be.

Oh yeah, I gagged.

"You're clean," he said enthusiastically.

"I should be," I coughed out, "you just hand washed, waxed and shined my throat. You need to towel dry it?"

"Nope, it's plenty dry."

He just shook his head and said that my Cancer Compadre (Shane, a neighbor who finished the same treatments a couple of months ahead of me) and I are "healing up so fast it's almost scary."

"Scary because you don't think you used enough radiation to get rid of the cancer?" I asked . . . rather quickly.

"No," he corrected himself. "Bad choice of words. Just that you two are about 6 months to a year ahead of what I've seen for this in the past."

"Once again, I'm above average," I smiled with a little head wobble and raised eyebrow.

Radiation Doc went on to say that the amount of radiation I was treated with was pretty much at the edge of diminishing returns. The fact that my taste buds work, I can chew and swallow and actually make a little bit of spit if I have to is what's impressive to him. Personally I'm not all that impressed with the minimal amount of saliva I have since I can't even eat spaghetti and meat sauce without a 1/2-gallon of water. Plus everything I put in my mouth still has to be lukewarm or it hurts my teeth. He said I need to be patient.

Yeah . . . that's so me.

I have put some effort in improving that total-lack-of-a-major-virtue. I made some great strides with it once when I coached T-ball, but since then I've had a few setbacks.

Just another learning experience offered up in cancer treatment.

responses

Hey Ed -- So glad to hear such good news!! And that sense of humor -- still hilarious (the "head wobble and raised eyebrow" made me laugh outloud!). I think if someone stuck their whole hand down my throat, I'd just throw up on them -- no question.

Wow. You've been through a lot -- well...God's brought you through a lot. What a testimony you have to share.

God is Good!! All the time!! Love you guys!

Amy & Clark

What terrific news, Ed and Debbie!

I'll share this in our prayer time at church.

Bert

Ed, Barb & I are overjoyed at your success; however,

we would think nothing less of a fanatical Hokie fan!

Go, man, go! Joe

Dear Ed,

Of course I haven't seen you in 28 years (wow), but the messages in your guestbook are certainly a testament to the life you've led.

My prayers are with you and your family. Best wishes for your continued recovery!

Julia

Yayyyyyyyyyyy!!!!!!!!!!

From yo momma (as if you couldn't tell)!

Ed, so glad to read the great news!

I thought of you and smiled yesterday when "Gimme Three Steps" came on the radio.

Remember when we had you sing that over and over again on that crazy Thanksgiving trip to TN? Love you,

Cammy

Hey Ed!

It is funny that you would mention patience...I was just writing to a "compadre," as you so well called your (also victorious) neighbor about the virtue of temperance, and I sought the ancient wisdom's insight. One of the sources I found for temperance tied it to other virtues and patience was included:

2 Peter 1:5-7 (King James Version)

5 And beside this, giving all diligence, add to your faith virtue; and to virtue knowledge;
6 And to knowledge temperance; and to temperance patience; and to patience godliness;
7 And to godliness brotherly kindness; and to brotherly kindness charity.

I think it's providential that "compadre" kindness and love finished the verses of ancient wisdom...

it seems you have found the inter-relational path to increasing the virtues and in so doing placed a confirming light on the path of your neighbor and us other compadres...thanks, bro!

Major

CaringBridge entry for April 4, 2009

This morning a young man, about 21, here in Manteo died with cancer.

I heard about Lamar last month through a friend of his who goes to my church, and I went by his house several times over the last month. I only got to meet his mom since he was asleep each time I swung by.

When I pulled into their driveway tonight I was delighted to see that it was packed with people. A grill was going, people were gathered all around the yard talking, there was laughter, the teenagers were playing basketball and the younger kids were playing in the sandbox and playhouse. I went up in the house to find Lamar's mom and gave her a hug. I told her how sorry I was for this day in her life and that Lamar had been lucky to have her there for him. I also said that it was clear she was not alone, but I was one more person who was praying for her, caring about her and she could call on if she needed anything.

As I drove away I stopped and looked back at the crowd there and thought of all of you. All the people who rallied around me and Debbie. Who sent cards and gifts, called, came by, offered up their encouragement through this site. I can't say it with enough enthusiasm, can't communicate clearly or loudly enough, so pay attention. I want you to get this point.

Thank you.

Thank you.

Thank you.

Your efforts, no matter how small you think they were, made all the difference in my experience. Your timing, no matter how random you think your comments were, was always perfect. The simple fact you showed that you were there was like getting a warm hug in person. And that's the lesson I'm taking away from this.

It's not a phrase I haven't heard before, but it's something that rings with a lot of clarity to me now:

You can pretend to care, but you cannot pretend to be there.

Being there matters. You were there for me. And reminded me not only how easy it is to make a difference in someone's life, but also how big a difference that can be.

Once again. Thank you.

responses

2 Corinthians 1:4 (New Living Translation)

4 He comforts us in all our troubles so that we can comfort others.

When they are troubled, we will be able to give them the same comfort God has given us.

Yeah, that's you...doing that.... Thanks for comforting Lamar's mom.

Janne

It has been a long time since I've been emotionally challenged, but you got me choked up with today's entry. WOW Ed...you can really feel the power of God's empathy for His people in that one. I'm thrilled to read the progress made this last couple of weeks. You have been through a ton of stuff but hopefully are now going to be able to fill out those size 32s a bit more soon.

Hope you have a Wonderful Easter!!

Celebrating Rebirth will take on a whole new meaning for me this year after reading your journal entries....

Makes me wish all the more that I hadn't lost touch with you and the rest of the MVHS gang when I moved back to CA. Doubt she'll remember me, but say hi to Mom for me. If you are up for it I'll follow-up with you later off-line.

Cheers, Ken

Ed,

That was a powerful entry. While I would love to accept your thanks, it was you who did the legwork. You were the one who endured all of the treatment, you were the one who never forgot to laugh during all of this, and it was you who found the courage to hold your head up high during the biggest challenge that you have ever faced.

So I can say with ease that it is I who need to thank you, for reminding me of so many things.

Among those, you reminded me to never give up, to cherish every moment, to cherish family and friends and that no matter how tough life may seem, there is always someone out there who will find a way to triumph. That person is you. So I am the one who needs to thank you.

Have a great weekend!

Best, Colin

Ed,

Everything from the heart is beautiful, and your entry is truly from the heart.

We thank you for showing us the proper way to handle such a tragedy in your life and still have the energy and compassion to reach out to others to help them deal with their problems.

This is truly how we as Christians should act.

May we, with God's help, and your example, be able to respond in like manner.

Proud to call you my Christian brother.

Dick

You are very welcome, my friend.

I am glad I could be just a small part in your healing by cheering you on.

You are a special person, and we need more like you. It was nice to read how you helped that boy's mom by being there. That's what always helps the most, being there in whatever form. I am proud to call you and Debbie my friends and will continue to keep you in my prayers. I hope to be able to see you out with us again soon. Take care and know you are loved.

Barb

Brother Ed, as Deb can probably attest,

I am usually not short on words...maybe height, character and other things...but when such love is genuinely spoken, words seem so inadequate.

As many have stated already, our thanks go to you for being there...fighting the fight that we hope to never face but pray that if we do, we face it with a little more strength because of what you gave to us. I am truly humbled to be a friend. Thank you.

Danny

Ed: Thank you -- for reminding us of those things that are important, family and friends, in the end there is no greater gift than to know that you have shared your life with such wonderful people who knew and cared about you.

We are all so busy, we need to be reminded that we may not be busy with things that matter.

Your postings have reminded of what is important, and what is not.

So thank you for wanting to share your experience with your family and friends. You have touched so many of us and we are the better for it.

Take care,
Your friend Jo Dee

I love you too, bro.

Donya

At some point in an experience like this, you realize that you're going to start a sentence with this very phrase:

The beginning (reprise)

Go ahead and reread that. I'll wait.

My point is that in any time of trial or suffering, we tend to have epiphanies. Realizations of something brand new to us or a sudden, strong reminder of something we used to know. I suppose when we're under extreme pressure for a prolonged period, we begin to notice things we normally miss as we saunter along through our days feeling, in the words of Pink Floyd, "comfortably numb." Some of these are larger than others and there's never only one. So, if we're telling someone about one of those "aha!" moments, we're probably going to use that phrase. Or at least I do, since I'm always telling somebody something.

Ergo: At some point in an experience like this, you realize how important the support of others is to your well being. Without it, a miserable experience is just that: miserable. With it, the experience becomes bearable or even beneficial in some way. Having friends, family and even strangers along for the ride helped me to find the positive moments and stay focused on them. A much better alternative than wallowing in the pain and fear that was there but had taken a back seat to the strength and humor that was still in me. To some folks it may have appeared I was just cruising through this on my own. Not so. I was cruising because there were people helping me stay up and because those people were encouraging me I felt some accountability to push on. To keep smiling. I may have had cancer, but I also had a terrific group of people who cared about me and kept letting me know it. That's something worth smiling about.

In the final few updates of my CaringBridge journal I thanked all the people who had visited me through that site. I also emailed other long distance supporters, called some folks, sent numerous cards and thanked the nearby individuals in person. Even now when I th nk of that time and that level of support I get choked up. It meant so much to me. And I knew I couldn't and wouldn't, let it stop there.

The realization of how my experience was influenced by the love of others and of the relative ease of my treatment inspired me to do something big. Which is pretty much how all my ideas start out. I can always scale back, right? Why not start out huge? An instructor I once had said, "If you're gonna go, go big." So every time we were asked a question we had to respond as if we were positive about the answer, even if we were just guessing. Loud and with confidence. This was not only entertaining for the class, but it really helped me learn the material quickly too. When I was right my confidence would soar and when I was wrong I was INCREDIBLY wrong. Either way I remembered the right answer from that point forward. Besides, everything goes better when it's done with enthusiasm.

So here's my idea: I want to change the world. I want to let every person on the earth know they are loved and I want to cure cancer.

Of course at this point I have no idea how I'm going to do this.

A Chinese philosopher pointed out that a journey of a thousand miles begins with a single step. My first steps came very easy. I didn't even know I was walking those thousand miles until I decided to at- tempt this book and looked back at my behavior.

Throughout my experience my attention kept being drawn to two areas: people I came across who were suffering with a serious illness and those who were working to improve the lives of the sick folks. Em- pathy for the ill and gratitude for the caregivers. I followed the example of my supporters and began to reach out.

You've already read about my conversation with Lamar's mom. I know I didn't do or say much, but from my experience on the side of the "encouragee" I know it wasn't wasted time. I have to admit that while I always felt compassion toward people in bad situations, I held back. Mainly because I didn't know what to say. Surprising, I know. I was afraid I would come across as insincere or as meddling, but this experi- ence has taught me otherwise. I don't think there's ever a time where saying, "I'm sorry you're going through this," is a bad thing. It will make a difference to the other person just to know someone cares about him or her. If there's more to do or say, it'll come naturally through the interaction that is rooted in caring and love. The guestbook entries I received proved to be somewhat of a resource to me. I could recall the things others said and make them my own. I learned from those entries that I didn't have to be brilliant or funny or even have experienced the pain someone else is going through to show that I care about them and offer my support. Lamar's mom may not even remember me individually down the road, but I'm certain she'll remember that there were people who loved her enough to be there during that time. She was not alone.

I began thinking of the second group of people after I first visited the cancer center where I would receive my radiation treatments. As the process was described to me I kept thinking of how much had to have gone into getting to that moment. My moment. My treatment. Everything in that center - the people, the supplies and the equipment represented years, decades, of hard work. And I got to benefit from it. Gratitude is too small a word.

As I went through treatment and my journal experience, I began to notice the entries where someone would say something about me doing things I do every day. The friend who said he got a boost just by seeing me smile and wave as we passed each other on the roads comes to mind. How easy is that? Smile and wave; brighten someone's day. Piece of cake. I'd get a little embarrassed by people using the words "awesome" and "amazing" to describe me going to work. But at the same time, it did make me feel like I was doing something impor-tant by tiling someone else's shower. I know having a really nice shower will turn something mundane into a more pleasurable experience. So that's a good thing I'm doing for them. But now I wanted to be the one noticing the other person's smile and wave then tell that person I was happy to see it and encourage them to keep on doing it. It made me feel great to hear I was doing something important just by being me. I should pass that feeling along to others.

I started with the folks at Siemens.

I never saw them drive by me or anything, but every day for 35 days, I would look up through my plastic mesh head restraint and see the Siemens logo on the machine that was whirring away and washing my neck with radiation. Some part of what turned the disease I had into Cancer Lite could be attributed to the people who designed, built and sold that machine. So I went online to Siemens' website and clicked on the "Contact Us" button. I filled out all the required information fields then typed in my "question" in the space provided. This is what I said:

"I was diagnosed with throat cancer in November 2008 and just finished up my radiation treatments a couple of months ago. Because of the incredible advances made in radiation therapy, the Outer Banks Cancer Center was able to tightly target the tumor and cancerous cells and greatly reduce the typical side effects experienced by head and neck radiation patients. Making what I had "Cancer Lite" and a surpris-ingly better experience than I anticipated. Every day at treatment I would look up at the Siemens logo on the machine and promise to thank you guys when this was over. It's over! So, thanks for developing and selling that machine. It made a big difference in my life as well as a bunch of other folks down here on the Outer Banks. Ed"

The very next day I got an email from a VP with Siemens Medical So-lutions telling me I had made her day. While saying that I "described the essence of what makes (them) come to work every day," she also made sure to credit the expertise of the "caring clinicians" who delivered my treatment. I have no doubt my simple thank you will be appreciated by many folks there, especially since they told me they're going to publish it in their company newsletter. I'm guessing they haven't gotten many thank you notes in the past. My hope is that everyone who reads it will sense my deep appreciation for their efforts and work with even more vigor to improve some already impressive technology.

And of course that little experience showed me just how far one thank you could go.

Changing the world, one person at a time.

I admit the second part of my idea has a little to do with relieving some of the guilt I feel about how easy I had it in this. There are hundreds of thousands of others who find out they have cancer and wind up in a truly difficult battle for their lives. And many won't win that battle. I am working to find ways to help support cancer research, improve treatment and continue toward a cure. If you haven't heard, we're moving in the right direction. Both mortality rates and occurrences of cancer are declining. Through continued diligence and effort, we could get everyone who's diagnosed to hear something like I heard: Two months of treatment and you'll be done. Or even better, vaccines to help us avoid cancer all together. A cure is possible, probable really, but it's going to take time, effort and money. Most importantly, it's going to take people. People doing a lot of different things but working

together to solve this problem. Some of those people will be scientists, doctors, nurses and techs; some will be patients. Others will be outside that loop acting as supporters giving their time, money or both. But all of them will be putting their hearts into whatever they choose as their role. I'm finding my role right now and I encourage you to find yours.

In my career as a Handyman I probably won't discover some wonder cure for cancer and I probably won't become one of the largest donors to the American Cancer Society (notice how I used the word "probably" there?). However, I can do a lot of things with the strengths I have.

For instance I'm a ham. I'm not likely to shy away from attention nor am I afraid of drawing some toward me. I'm also persistent, or stubborn, depending on how you look at it. And I'm a decent athlete. So I've entered the Outer Banks Marathon this November. I know it's almost becoming cliché - running a marathon after a life-threatening illness but it fits. Especially with the timing. The race is going to be held on November 8, 2009.

That is one year and one day after I found out I had cancer. On that day I'll be running the first marathon of my life. In that single year I was diagnosed, was treated and then trained my way into shape to run 26 miles. Not too shabby if I can pull it off.

I was talking to a friend of mine, Jeff, about that guilty feeling I had now and then and he said, "Don't feel guilty; you're the one people need to see." He told me I was "hope" because I was doing so well. I suppose that's true to some extent and I thought if I'm the one they need to see, then I should do something worth watching. Now every day I update my training log on Facebook, friends respond with encouragement and some have started exercising, too. I let them know I'm thankful for their encouragement, that I love them for being there and encourage them to keep reaching out to others.

The world's beginning to change.

I don't think I will ever say that I'm glad I had cancer, but I am glad that I experienced it the way I did. I'm eternally grateful for the people who experienced it with me and loved me through it.

And I plan on living and sharing that love for as long as I can.

Six months after my final treatment, and not quite five months after The Plague,

I ran 14 miles.

Even though I grabbed some Gatorade, hit the bathroom and walked some as I came by my house at the ten mile mark, I covered the distance averaging just under eight minutes per mile. I had not run that far or that fast since I was in high school running cross-country and track. Even more impressive was the fact that I had gained weight during my training and was back up to 145 pounds. Once again, the help of family and friends (primarily in the form of training, diet, and rehab advice) played a prime role in my success.

I am truly amazed at how strong I had gotten in such a short period of time. Even though I still had a long way to go in order to cover the full 26 miles 385 yards of the Outer Banks Marathon, my confidence was soaring. I had beaten Cancer Lite and come back better than before.

ED... IT WAS **MALIGNANT**.

Just before that particular training run I had gone in for my six month PET scan. This was a full body scan to confirm what was being seen by my surgeon every month that I was clean and cancer free.

At my regularly scheduled appointment with him after the scan he told me, "We got your PET scan results back and there's a small dark spot in the right lymph node in your neck."

I instantly stayed still without altering my facial expression and told myself, "Hear him out. Don't panic."

He went on, "The radiologist and I both think that it may be nothing, an inflammation maybe, since it is so small."

I remembered having a few mouth sores show up around that time but they went away so quickly after hitting the Biotene rinse a couple of more times a day that I wondered if my system had been dealing with whatever that was.

"We'll just keep a close eye on things over the next couple of appointments," he said, "but first let's take a quick feel to see if I can find any lump."

He then proceeded to put his hand down my throat and rub the right side.

Yep. I gagged pretty good.

"Sorry about that," he told me. "Try to relax."

"Of course I will," I thought.

He didn't feel a thing and told me that he thought I was good to go,

but that he would be adding the internal throat-massage thing to the scope-up-the-nose-and-down-the-throat thing he already did at those appointments.

Lovely.

I asked him about a couple of oddities I had developed in the weeks between our appointments. One of which was every time I looked down I felt a sort of tug and tingling sensation all the way down my spine and into my legs. He thought it might be some sort of fibrosis and suggested I ask Radiation Doc about it.

I called him on the way home and told him about that and the PET scan.

"The sensation you're feeling isn't fibrosis, but is well documented among head and neck radiation patients," he told me. "That will get better over time as you continue to heal from the treatments. As for the scan," he continued, "I want to see the disk and have a radiologist I know who has a great deal of experience in looking at people in your situation to see it too."

Bottom line was he didn't like it. I remembered how in my first meeting with him, when he was talking about radiation therapy and went over the release form with all of the side effects. The phrase "secondary malignancies" popped into my head.

I called the surgeon's office and had the disk sent over to Radiation Doc's office on the Outer Banks, and I drove up to get it and deliver it.

I can't say I was all that worried about it. I knew that I had talented, caring people all over my situation and if it was cancer again we would have caught it very early and could treat it right away. That's why I had the monthly visits and scheduled scans to begin with, right? Still, the thought of going through radiation again, maybe adding chemo to the mix and possibly even surgery was not a pleasant scenario to ponder. And how would all of that affect my training and running the marathon? Didn't matter to me if I crawled the thing, I was going to do it. But the purpose behind completing the race would be drastically different than it was right now.

The very next day I got a call from Radiation Doc's office and they told me it was just an inflammation. No sign of cancer at all.

"Sweet!" I told her, and was surprised at how relieved I was at the news. I didn't think I had been all that tense but apparently I was.

That whole experience got me thinking about my follow up schedule and the fact that I wouldn't be pronounced cured for 5 years. While no trouble is expected for me, I am going to be reminded that I am not out of the woods for years and years to come. What about those that don't have my prognosis? What do they feel knowing that with each appointment, each scan, a pair of dice is rolling and if one of a couple of numbers comes up they have cancer again? Regardless of statistics, I will be thinking about those dice every time I go through a test. Every cancer survivor is faced with it. It's not really over even when it's over.

So what do I do with that? The only thing I can really do is what all of us have to do: Live the life we've got.

I think, though, to really live this life we have to live it for others more than for ourselves. Regardless of how lousy our situation might be, there is room for compassion and caring for someone else. So live your life and help me change the world. Take a look at the things all of us have at our disposal: talents we were born with, skills we've developed, and the circumstances of our lives then put yours to work for those around you.

Then live.
Really live.